The Universe

© contmedia GmbH
www.contmedia.com
Concept and Layout: contmedia GmbH
Naumann & Göbel Verlagsgesellschaft mbH, Cologne
English translation: Malve von Hassell

ISBN 3-625-21130-0

All pictures not otherwise specified: the contmedia GmbH archive

Universe

Star Systems • Planets • Galaxies

NAUMANN & GÖBEL

Contents

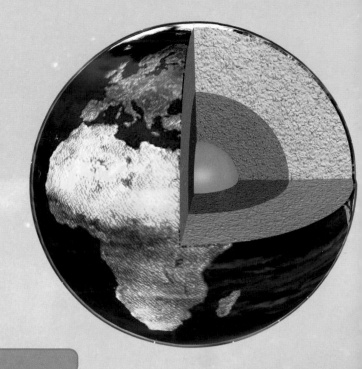

GALAXIES 58

STAR SYSTEMS 66

IMAGES OF THE ZODIAC 80

APPENDIX 90

Cosmos/ Cosmology

The Greek term "cosmos" refers to the universe and to a world order perceived as harmonious. Cosmology is a science that has as its object of inquiry the origins, development, and structure of the universe as an integrated entity. In cosmogony, a sub-field of astronomy, scientists traditionally concern themselves with issues such as the origins and development of celestial bodies and the question of how the universe began.

These questions have occupied human beings for millennia. Stonehenge, a circle of standing stones in the south of England, served religious purposes as well as the observation of the Sun and the Moon for hundreds of years. The pyramids of Gizeh also represented far more than graves. Their builders exhibited considerable astronomical competence in the alignment of the monuments. The ancient Greeks developed the geocentric worldview. According to this perspective, the Earth is at the centre of the universe. The Sun, the Moon, and the stars orbit around it. Proponents of this theory such as Pythagoras and Aristotle encountered opposition already in their own lifetimes.

In the late Middle Ages, Nicolaus Copernicus established a heliocentric worldview, supported by scientific evidence. However, his work was ignored for a long time and eventually was banned. Galileo Galilei and Johannes Kepler built on the various theories of Copernicus and developed them further. Giordano Bruno, a charismatic scientist, was the first to argue that the universe is infinite and that the stars are other suns. His convictions cost him his life; he died on the stake in Rome in 1600. Most people were more than reluctant to accept that human beings and their planet are not at the centre of the universe.

Universe

When we look up at the bright night sky, the number of stars seems unlimited. Yet with our bare eyes we can perceive at most 3,000. Only the most powerful telescope turns this apparent limitlessness into a virtual reality. Such a telescope makes possible the observation of thousands of galaxies and star clusters with thousands of millions of stars. According to estimates, there are 100 thousand million galaxies. Every single one of these in turn contains 100 thousand million stars.

Super cluster

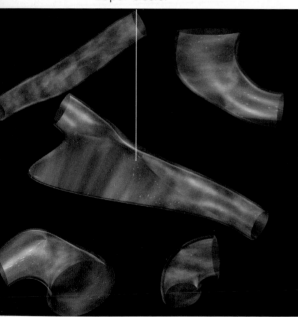

Super clusters are collections of tens of thousands of galaxies. These are held together in clusters or groups by gravity.

It is obvious that nobody could make any precise statement about the space occupied by all these planetary bodies. Such enormous dimensions call for special ways of describing distance. The commonly used term "light-year" refers to the distance covered by light in the space of one year. The units of measurement of distance commonly used on Earth would hardly serve in this context.

One light-year is the equivalent of a distance of 9,461,000,000,000 (9,461 thousand million) kilometres.

Estimates of when the universe began diverge greatly. They range from 10 to 20 thousand million years ago, with a recent tendency in favour of the greater figure. Since this zero point in time, the universe has been continually expanding.

This understanding is based on the concept of the recession of galaxies. The light arriving on Earth tends to shift increasingly towards red in the range of spectral colours, the further away from Earth a respective galaxy is located. This process is known as redshift. Since red has the greatest wavelength (violet has the shortest wavelength), it has been possible to prove the recession effect on the basis of concrete evidence. The example of sound waves helps to illustrate this process. When a motorcycle overtakes you, the tone of the disappearing motorcycle becomes deeper – the sound waves are stretched. There is an analogous process in the case of spectral colours.

Edwin Hubble, the astronomer after whom the Hubble Space Telescope was named, discovered that the speed with which galaxies move apart increases with the distance between them. For instance, according to Hubble's law, when a galaxy is ten times as far away from Earth as the Magellan Cloud, it also moves away from us at ten times the speed.

Galaxies consist of thousands of millions of stars. Together with approximately 30 other galaxies, the Milky Way, within which our solar system is located, is part of the local group. Larger collections are referred to as galaxy clusters. These in turn form the so-called super clusters. The Local Group is part of the Virgo super cluster which extends across an expanse of 100 thousand million light-years, no more than an unremarkable little spot. Along their edges super clusters form barriers that have a structure akin to a honeycomb. Between these barriers there are spaces of immeasurable distance – according to some calculations there are about 300 thousand million light-years of expanses that contain almost no stars at all. Despite the nearly endless number of celestial bodies, the universe is ultimately a rather lonely place. Volumetric calculations indicate 1 atom per 10 cubic metres of space.

Big Bang

Today it is generally accepted that everything began with a great explosion, the so-called Big Bang, roughly 15 to 20 thousand million years ago. How did we arrive at this number?

The American astronomer Edwin Hubble offers the following explanation. He developed the concept of the mathematical constant according to which the speed with which galaxies travel away from each other increases with the distance between them. Hence, the recession velocity is approximately 75 kilometres/second per one million parsecs (1 parsec = 3.25 light-years) of distance. Given the fact that everything is drifting apart, one can conclude that the matter of the universe must have been united at one point.

If we reverse the Hubble effect, using the same constant value, we arrive at a general time frame when the universe was presumably born. Science cannot offer a more precise date. There is a great deal of uncertainty regarding the first period after the Big Bang. For instance, it has not been possible to determine whether there were perhaps delays in the process of expansion. The only thing we know for sure is that all matter was once together in one place at the greatest possible level of density. This is based on the fact that lightweight matter (hydrogen and helium) can be found within the oldest stars. Furthermore, there is a process that might be described as post-partum afterpains of the Big Bang. Here we are referring to cosmic background radiation, first discovered in 1965 by the American scientists Penzias and Wilson, who used a radio telescope.

Immediately after the Big Bang, in the lightning phase, i.e. less than one millionth of a second, the temperature was still enormously high (50,000 thousand million degrees Kelvin),

despite the process of expansion already beginning. This radiation created particles and antiparticles. These became photons, in other words radiation that in turn created particles and antiparticles. Their expansion process was unimaginably rapid. Within one second, the radius had already reached 4 light-years.

Compared to the initial phase, it had by now become practically chilly (10–15 thousand million degrees

Kelvin). After a few minutes, the temperature dropped to 1 thousand million degrees, with a density approximately equivalent to iron. The first helium cores formed out of protons and neurons.

The Big Bang was finished 100,000 years later. The radius of expansion had now reached 7 million light years. From this point on, matter was being formed and the phase of the radiation universe was over.

According to cosmological theories, the universe began to expand all of a sudden as result of a tremendous explosion about 15–20 thousand million years ago. This zero point in the cosmological calendar is referred to as the Big Bang.

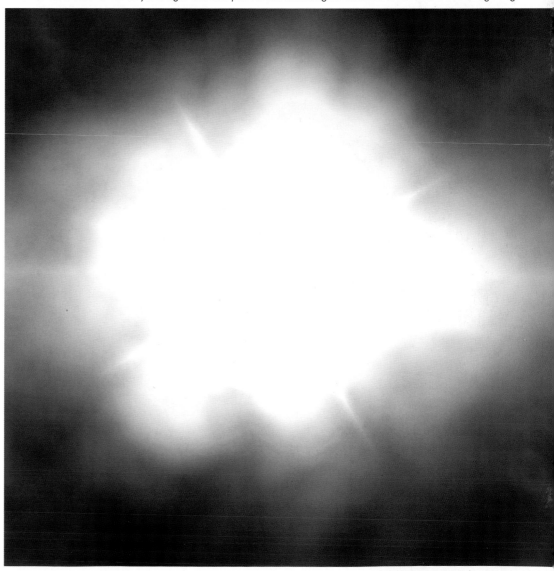

Symbols/Units

There are certain international symbols for the identification of individual planets in our solar system that are recognized all over the world.

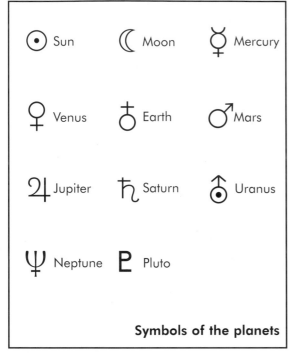

☉ Sun	☾ Moon	☿ Mercury
♀ Venus	♁ Earth	♂ Mars
♃ Jupiter	♄ Saturn	⛢ Uranus
♆ Neptune	♇ Pluto	

Symbols of the planets

Various systems, generally described three-dimensionally in astronomy, are used to determine the individual positions of the constellations in space. These are:

- **Topocentric coordinates**
- **Geocentric coordinates**
- **Heliocentric coordinates**
- **Galactocentric coordinates**

Topocentric coordinates refer to the position of a celestial body as seen from the actual point of observation, in other words from the Earth. **Geocentric coordinates** refer to the determination of an object from an imaginary point of observation within the centre of the Earth. **Heliocentric coordinates** refer to an imagined point in the centre of the Sun. **Galactocentric coordinates** refer to the centre of the Milky Way (not to be confused with galactic coordinates).

In order to determine the height of a constellation, one uses the horizon system. It is based on the horizon as the basic circle. The vertical line on the horizontal plane transverses the celestial body at the zenith (crown) and the nadir (foot) as celestial pole.

The celestial equator divides the celestial sphere into a northern and a southern hemisphere. The rotational axis of the Earth is perpendicular to this equator line and transverses the celestial sphere at the celestial north pole and the celestial south pole. The distance of a celestial body from the equator is referred to as a declination. We distinguish between a locally fixed and a moving equator system.

Ecliptic is the term used to describe the celestial circle or "path" that the Sun travels within the space of one year along the celestial sphere, as seen from the perspective of the Earth. The ecliptic system is determined by the coordinates of the ecliptic and the North and South Poles.

The astronomical unit AU is used for describing distance in astronomy. It was determined by the International Astronomical Union (IAU) and refers to the average distance between the Sun and the Earth (1 AU = 149.6 x 106 km (approx. 150,000,000 km).

Another commonly used unit for measuring distance is the "parsec". A star is at a distance of 1 parsec if the average distance Earth–Sun (AU), as seen from the star, becomes visible at 1 arcsecond. Parsec is a compound word made up of "parallax" and "second". 1 pc (par-sec) represents 206,265 AU. The term "light-year" is more familiar. It refers to the distance (not the time!) travelled by light over the course of one year. That is, approximately 10 thousand million kilometres (1 LY) = 0.3065 pc = 63,240 AU.

Ufologists and scientists have been anticipating contact with extraterrestrial beings for almost a century. However, to date it has not been possible to receive and identify any signals. There are various special messages contained on board the space probe Pioneer 10 that report about us in the event of any possible extraterrestrial intelligence encountering the probe.

Is Anybody Out There?

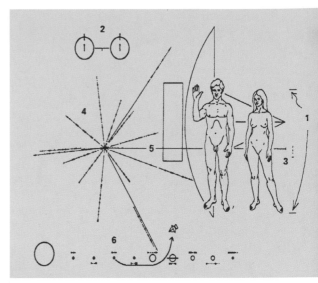

Calling card from Earth
The space probe Pioneer 10, sent into space in 1972, carries the first message to help facilitate contact with extraterrestrials. Scientists created a poster that shows human beings, the solar system, the location of the Sun, etc.

There is hardly any other issue as controversial as the question as to whether or not there is extraterrestrial life. As early as 400 BC, Metrodorus of Chios wrote the following: "To assume that the Earth is the only inhabited world in infinity is as absurd as the idea that only one seed in an entire acre would germinate." Given the unimaginably large number of stars, this theory is entirely compelling. However, many prerequisites are required in order to produce life on a given planet. The rotational velocity must not be too high or too low. The planet must be large enough to be able to bind an atmosphere to itself. Water is indispensable. The correct distance from the Sun is relevant. The temperature cannot always be either above boiling or below freezing.

In our solar system, Venus and Mars, the immediate neighbours of Earth, are already too hot or too cold respectively. A harmonious relationship of elements on the planet in question is also critical. In addition, the associated sun must also contribute to life-sustaining conditions.

The age, size, volume, and amount of radiated energy are some of the parameters that can facilitate the development of life on a planet – however, only when they are within certain limits.

Stars in double or multiple systems are eliminated, as are those stars that are irregular in their radiation. Of course, this list is by no means complete, serving only as an illustration. Indeed, we do not actually know exactly how many criteria must be fulfilled. According to a theoretical mathematical calculation by Prof. Hoimar von Ditfurth, there are at least 12 thousand million possibilities in the Milky Way alone. Furthermore, he also points out that even this enormous selection might still not be large enough. What would be the result if there were only 35 minimum requirements for the development of life? Ditfurth offers a statistical thought exercise to respond to this question: "If there were one player, continually throwing a die without any interruptions, on each of the 12 thousand million possible planets, then 6 thousand million years later just one of these would have succeeded in throwing a winning number 35 times in a row."

Even if there are other places in the universe where life has developed, we most likely will never learn about them. In order to be able to surmount these unimaginable distances in the universe, one would have to be able to move beyond the limitations of the laws of physics. It is incontrovertible that matter cannot move faster than the speed of light. Nevertheless, the search for extraterrestrial life continues even within the context of scientific inquiries.

The space probe Pioneer 10 represents the equivalent of a message in a bottle, launched into space in 1972. One of its panels shows our solar system with its location in the galaxy. If ET were to find this space probe one day, we would still have to wait several million years for a response.

Radio astronomy has been used to search the skies for radio signals in a systematic fashion. In 1974 a three-minute radio signal was sent from Earth in the direction of a globular cluster of stars in the constellation Hercules. The unknown recipient will not receive this message until 20,000 years later.

In the final analysis, extraterrestrial life is certainly possible, but contact appears rather doubtful. In this context, it is appropriate to mention a graffito that has become famous. An American student wrote the following on a wall at his university: "Is there intelligent life on Earth?" Shortly afterward, an unknown respondent wrote: "Yes, but I am only visiting."

Solar System

Moving counterclockwise, nine planets with their respective moons orbit our central star, the Sun. The planets' orbits are tilted towards each other only slightly; in other words, they are moving along in nearly the same plane. The planet Mercury is closest to the Sun. The others are Venus, Earth, Mars, Jupiter, Saturn, Uranus, Neptune and Pluto, in that order.

The first four (Mercury, Venus, Earth and Mars) have relatively little mass, no atmosphere at all or only a thin one, and a stony surface. By contrast, the four giant planets Jupiter, Saturn, Uranus and Neptune, located outside the so-called asteroid belt, have a great deal of mass, but no firm surface. Furthermore, the large planets are surrounded by a powerful atmosphere.

How was it possible that a system with one star and several planets could develop? Parts of an interstellar gas and dust cloud compressed and thus formed a star. Increasing pressure resulted in processes of nuclear fusion, causing the star to glow. The new sun bound the surrounding gas and dust cloud to itself by force of gravity. Like the rings of Saturn, this cloud orbited the central star. The large-mass areas within the cloud attracted more matter and continued to compress. Their gravity produced spherical shapes – the planets. Smaller areas of compression that were not captured by the large-mass planets orbit these large planets as their moons.

The Sun

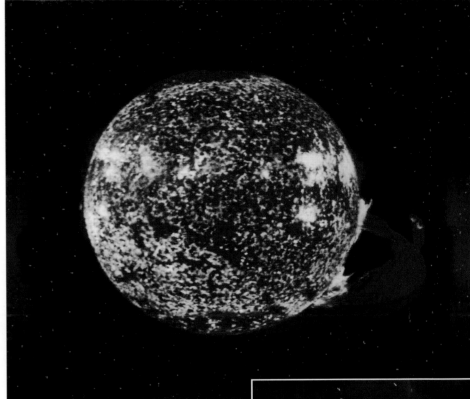

Interesting processes can be observed on the Sun, the central star in our planetary system. Its granular surface is in a constant state of activity as a result of sudden energy discharges and gas eruptions.

The Sun is the centre of our planetary system. With a diameter of 1,392,530 kilometres, this huge ball of gas is almost 110 times as large as the Earth. The Sun performs a complete rotation on its axis once every 26.8 days.

The Sun's mass consists of 78.4 percent hydrogen and 19.8 percent helium. There are smaller amounts of oxygen (approx. 0.86 percent), carbon (approx. 0.4 percent), and iron (approx. 0.15 percent) at the surface of the Sun, also described as the photosphere.

Surface temperatures are around 5,800 EC. Moving towards the interior of the Sun, temperatures rise to several million EC. Here, nuclear reactions take place; i.e., hydrogen is constantly being turned into helium. The resulting energy spreads as radiation. This in turn causes matter to move; hot matter is passed to the irregular surface of the Sun while cooler matter moves towards the centre. These currents result in eruptions on the surface, creating a constant gas vortex. The Sun's atmosphere consists of three layers. One is the photosphere, already mentioned above; the chromosphere and the corona are located at lower levels, both with a lesser gas density.

The Sun as a Star

Actually, the Sun is a perfectly ordinary fixed star with an average size like other stars. It is located at a distance of roughly 12 parsecs in the northern region of our galaxy's plane. The distance between the Sun and the galaxy's centre is 7,700 parsecs. Moving at a speed of approximately 220 kilometres per second on a nearly circular path, the Sun orbits the centre of the galaxy once in 210 million years.

Yet there is something that distinguishes this star from other celestial bodies. It facilitates life on Earth and influences this life in a decisive manner.

As a supplier of energy, the Sun provides the very foundation for the origin of life. It determines the seasons and the length of each day.

Every second, the Sun transforms 4 million tons of matter into electromagnetic radiation that arrives on the Earth as light, warmth, X-rays and ultraviolet radiation. This process of combustion has been repeating itself over and over again since the birth of the Sun 5 thousand million years ago and, according to the calculations of astrophysi-

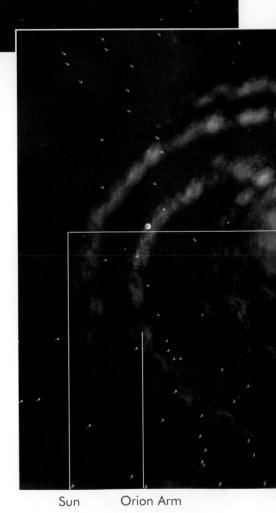

Sun   Orion Arm

14

cists, is supposed to continue for another 5 thousand million years.

Until as recently as half a century ago, we had only a limited understanding of where the Sun's energy comes from. However, Albert Einstein had recognized already in 1905 that energy can transform itself into matter and that in turn matter actually represents a form of energy. This theory became critical for all future inquiries. Einstein expressed it in his famous formula: $E = mc^2$ (energy = mass times the speed of light squared).

On the basis of the assumption that the Sun's energy results from core fusions, the physicists von Weizsäcker and Bethe discovered in 1938 that the transformation of hydrogen into helium in the interior

Milky Way

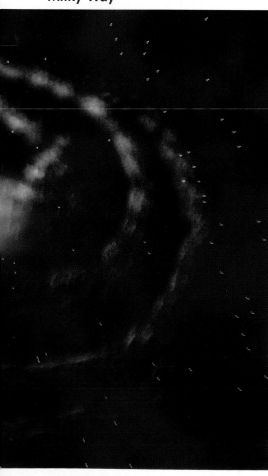

Given its particular structure, the Milky Way, with a diameter of 100,000 light-years, is counted among the spiral-shaped galaxies. Our Sun is located on one of these arms, the so-called Orion Arm, at a distance of approximately 32,000 light-years from the galactic centre. It is the central star of our planetary system.

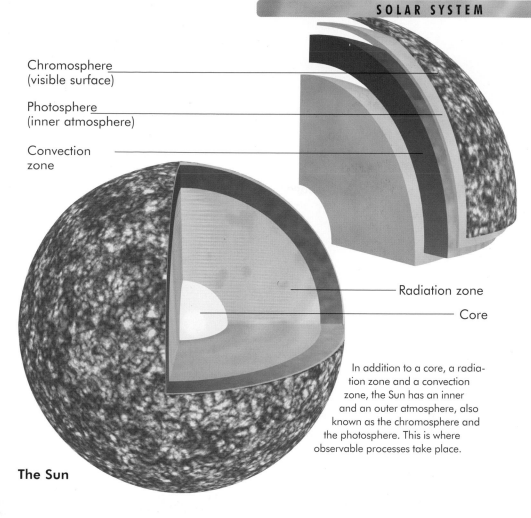

Chromosphere (visible surface)

Photosphere (inner atmosphere)

Convection zone

Radiation zone

Core

The Sun

In addition to a core, a radiation zone and a convection zone, the Sun has an inner and an outer atmosphere, also known as the chromosphere and the photosphere. This is where observable processes take place.

of the Sun produces energy. On the basis of their calculations, astrophysicists predict that once the Sun's entire supply of hydrogen has been transformed into helium, the Sun will first expand into a red giant and subsequently shrink down to the size of a white dwarf that will cool out gradually.

The Structure of the Sun

According to physical calculations, the temperatures in the interior reach approximately 15 million EC. Here, core reactions take place that result in the production of energy and hence the Sun's radiation.

In the course of the transformation of matter into solar energy, a proton (the core of the hydrogen

atom) fuses with another proton to form deuterium.

In this process, one particle is transformed into a neutron. At the same time, a neutron particle and a positron particle are sent into space; however, these are almost entirely without mass.

Other reactions occur between the newly formed deuterium and another proton. This produces helium-3 (one neutron and two protons). This in turn reacts with another helium-3 particle, forming helium-4 with two protons and two neutrons each. The remaining two protons in turn react in other combinations.

In every one of these reactions, a portion of mass is transformed into energy. This energy travels as radiation across a 380,000-kilometre-thick radiation zone to the adjoining convection zone. From this 140,000-kilometre-thick zone, energy moves up to the photosphere, the visible surface of the Sun, where it leaves the Sun as light and warmth. In the photosphere, temperatures reach a mere 5,500 EC.

The visible photosphere exhibits variable degrees of brightness. Bubble-like apparitions, also referred to as granules, change repeatedly in intervals of approximately ten minutes. The cause for this can be found in the convection zone of the Sun's interior.

We can recognize the heat rising up in the hot gas clouds. Similar to the waves associated with an earthquake, the Sun is subject to surface vibrations, the expansion of which depends on the condition of the various currents in the Sun's interior as well as the relationship between temperature and density levels there.

The middle atmospheric layer, also known as the chromosphere, and the outer atmosphere, or corona, adjoin the 400-kilometre-thick photosphere. The chromosphere, located between the photosphere and the corona, is up to 10,000 kilometres thick. The prevailing temperatures reach 10,000 EC.

The structure is complicated. Bristlelike gas currents, also known as spicules, up to 1,000 kilometres thick, shoot as high as 3,000 to 10,000 kilometres. Just a few minutes later, they collapse again. Astronomers assume that this is

The Sun's energy is the result of nuclear fusions in its centre. Beginning with the fusion of protons in the hydrogen nucleuses, there is whole series of reactions to develop the high-energy gamma rays that reach us as light, once they have worked their way to the surface of the Sun.

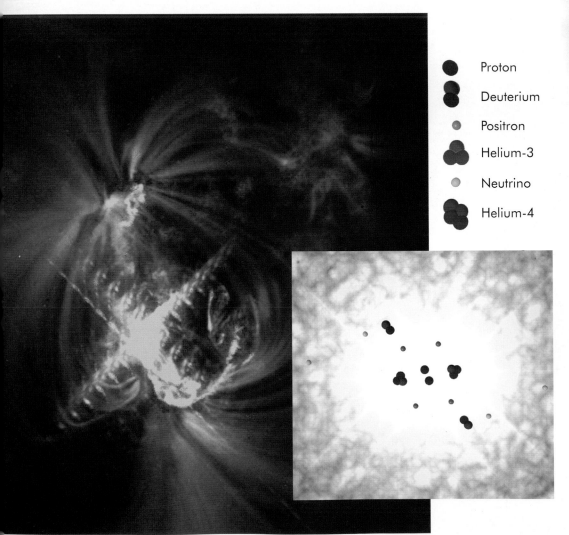

Proton

Deuterium

Positron

Helium-3

Neutrino

Helium-4

linked to the effect of magnetic fields. The adjoining corona expands further into interplanetary space; it can be observed right before and after a total solar eclipse and reaches temperatures of up to 2 million EC. The corona's shape changes slightly, depending on the level of solar activity.

Thus, during those times when sunspots are at a minimum, the corona appears to be flatter at the poles and wider at the equator. The corona's rays are particularly noticeable.

Here, matter appears to have greater density than elsewhere. This is probably due to the strong magnetic fields.

The so-called solar wind streams out of the corona. Consisting of electrons and protons (charged subatomic particles), it moves away from the Sun at a speed of 3 million

Solar Activity

The spicules of the chromosphere and the granules of the photosphere, part of our image of the Sun, can be found across the entire solar surface. In addition, there are activities that are limited by time and space. These include, among others, the so-called sunspots. These mostly occur in groups. Some have a diameter of only a few 100 kilometres and can be observed over the course of several days, while others reach up to 50,000 kilometres in diameter and in some instances remain visible for several months.

Sunspots are caused by strong magnetic fields that break the flow of heat in areas of the photosphere. Thus, they limit the amount of

energy flowing outward. The temperature within sunspots is consequently up to 2,000 EC lower than that in the surrounding layer, the photosphere; this in turn makes the sunspots appear to be darker. The dark core area is called the umbra. It is surrounded by the penumbra, with a bright fringe and a ray-like structure.

Sunspot activity occurs in cycles of approximately 11 years. For the most part, sunspots appear in pairs at the beginning of a new cycle, in particular in the vicinity of the poles. This phase is called "sunspot minimum".

Beginning with approximately three sunspots, their number increases steadily, while moving closer and closer to the equator until reaching the sunspot maximum of approximately 90 sunspots.

Solar eruptions

Protuberances (gas eruptions from the chromosphere)

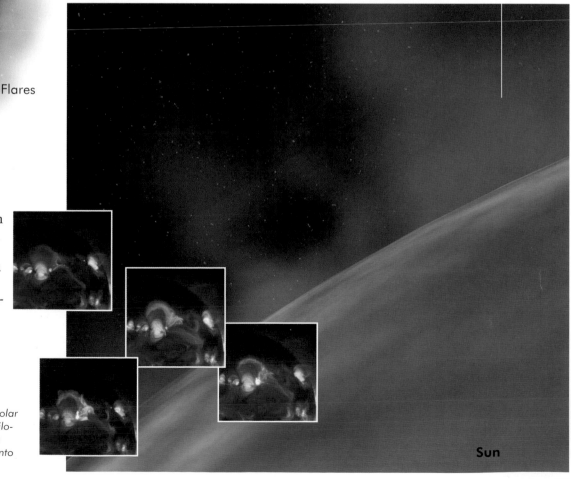

kilometres per hour. It forms the heliosphere, which contains magnetic fields and electric currents and fills the space of the solar system that to us looks empty. The heliosphere shields our planetary system against cosmic radiation.

Flares

Gas eruptions along the edge of the solar disk reach heights of up to 100,000 kilometres. They are called protuberances and sometimes shoot out all the way into outer space.

Sun

This sequence of events is repeated every 11 years, notwithstanding a few deviations. Astronomers assume that irregular solar rotation (faster rotation at the equator than at the poles) results in a shift of magnetically active zones in the direction of the equator.

In the immediate vicinity of sunspots it is often possible to observe solar flares. These flares are also directly linked to the magnetic areas at both poles. Solar flares can be observed as veritable explosions of light. From the photosphere they stretch upward by as much as 20,000 kilometres and reach as far as the corona. Supposedly, their activities are linked to the fact that strong magnetic fields build up energy, culminating in these sudden eruptions.

Gas eruptions at the edge of the solar disk, described as protuberances, are particularly impressive. These reach heights of several 100,000 kilometres. During a solar eclipse, an observer can see them as bright arches. In the light, they have the appearance of thread-like structures (filaments). These gas eruptions as well are connected to the strong magnetism associated with sunspots and have a lifespan of several months. For the most part, protuberances and filaments remain in the chromosphere; sometimes, however, they shoot out into outer space.

Sunspot cycle

1st year

4th year

7th year

10th year

12th year

Sunrise and Sunset

Since time immemorial, our life on Earth has been determined by the regular change of day and night. This was even more the case before technology presented us with artificial light. But why is it light during the day and dark at night? Because the Earth rotates within the space of one day, which consists of 24 hours.

At the end of one night, the Sun rises on the horizon in the east. The show begins with the dawn. The Sun is still at an oblique angle towards the Earth's atmosphere; consequently, sunlight passes only through the upper layers of air. These break the light, resulting in the increased brightness in the sky that is called twilight. The steeper the angle of the Sun on the horizon in the course of a morning, the brighter is the sky.

Throughout the day, the sky appears radiantly blue, unless it is covered by clouds. The British astronomer Lord Raleigh discovered that this brightness is created when sunlight is reflected by molecules and atoms in the atmosphere.

The particles that scatter the sunlight are significantly smaller than the light's wavelength. Since the dispersion of shorter waves (for us visible as blue light) is much stronger than the dispersion of longer waves (for us visible as red light), the daytime sky appears to be blue. This colouration then hides all other phenomena in the solar system, such as planets and stars, except for the Sun and the Moon. On rare occasions, Venus and Jupiter stand out in terms of their colouration and are visible. Aside from those instances, during the day one gains the impression that, other than the Sun, the Moon and the Earth, there is nothing else in our solar system.

At midday, the Sun illuminates the atmosphere evenly across the

The Sun rises every morning on the horizon in the east. The dispersion of sunlight occurs as it passes through several layers of air, thus producing a brightness in the sky that is referred to as twilight. As the Sun's angle toward the horizon becomes increasingly steeper in the course of the day, the light changes and the sky appears to be bright and clear. Toward the afternoon, the Sun once again approaches a flatter angle toward the horizon. After another twilight has begun in the transitional phase, the Sun finally disappears in the evening behind the horizon in the west.

entire horizon. At this time, the Sun appears to be slightly more yellow; even rainy areas in the distance have a yellow tint. This is due to the scattering of sunlight entering from directly above. At the end of the day, the Sun tilts towards the western horizon. Now its rays must pierce through a thicker atmospheric layer. At this point, the light dispersion that we had perceived as blue loses its short wave component. First, the yellow colouration of the Sun appears to be darker; then it shifts towards red before disappearing behind the horizon. As soon as the Sun goes down behind the western horizon, a reddish earth shadow appears in the east, and the blue tones of the sky get darker until the earth shadow has reached the sky. At this point, the first stars appear. Astronomical twilight begins when the Sun has reached an angle of 18 degrees below the horizon. Until this moment, the upper layers of air that reflect the light are still within reach of the sunlight.

The length of one day, that is, the time between sunrise and sundown, depends on the season and the geographical latitude of the observer's location.

Mercury

Mercury is named after the Roman god of commerce and travel. With a mean distance of only 57.9 million kilometres, it is the planet closest to the Sun. It has a diameter of 4,880 kilometres and is the second smallest planet in our solar system. The only smaller one is Pluto. Mercury's orbit is very elliptical and tilted towards the orbits of the other planets. The American space probe Mariner 10 was the first spacecraft to obtain more detailed information about Mercury. The space probe flew past the planet in 1974. The surface looked like the lunar surface, and the atmosphere appeared to be very thin.

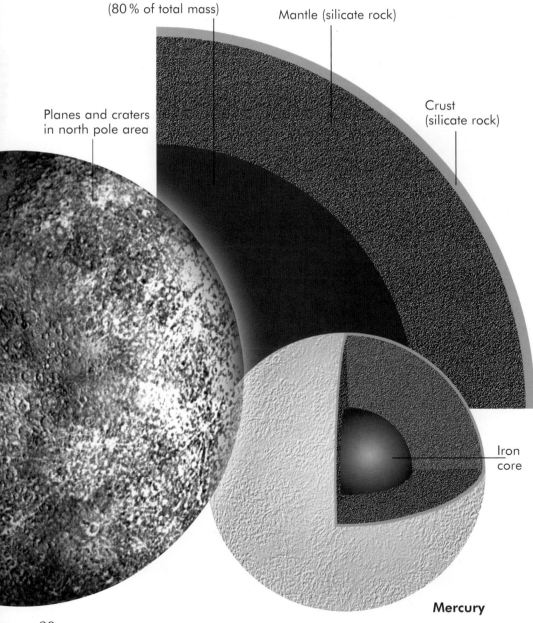

Iron core
(80 % of total mass)

Mantle (silicate rock)

Planes and craters
in north pole area

Crust
(silicate rock)

Iron
core

Mercury

57,910,000 km

Orbit

Mercury is the innermost planet in our solar system; it is closest to our central star. The distance to the Sun fluctuates between 46 million and 70 million kilometres. This reflects the highly elliptical shape of the orbit. Mercury's orbit and that of two other planets (Pluto and Mars)

20

Mercury

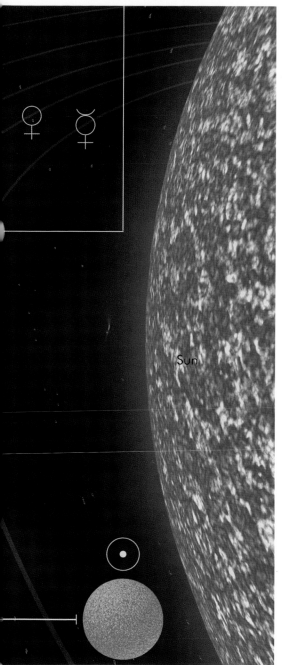

Sun

From the Earth you can observe Mercury only for a short time just before sunrise or after sundown. In the evening, Mercury can be seen when it is on the left, eastern side. The greatest possible angular separation is referred to as the greatest eastern elongation from the Sun. In turn, in the early morning hours Mercury can be seen on the right hand or west of the Sun. The greatest angular separation from the Sun is referred to here as the greatest western elongation from the Sun. Visibility lasts for no more than two hours respectively.

Surface

In the 1920s, the astronomer Antoniadi prepared the first images of Mercury's surface. He identified various dark and light spots and discovered apparent cloud layers. We only gained new information once the space probe Mariner 10 passed by the planet and took photographs. According to these photographs, the surface looks very much like the lunar surface.

There are many impact craters on Mercury just as on the Moon. These craters are called rupes. They were probably formed when the planet was born, about 4 thousand million years ago, and the core of the planet began to cool and contract.

Aside from hydrogen, the thin helium atmosphere contains only minor traces of sodium and oxygen, and even less neon, argon and potassium; it cannot bind clouds to itself. This is due to the limited mass of the planet. The mean density of 5.43 grams per cubic centimetre is comparable to the density of Earth. Astronomers believe that Mercury has a core of iron and nickel.

Morning and Evening Visibility

Because of its relative proximity to the Sun, Mercury can be seen only rarely. It is visible only shortly before sunrise and after sundown. In our latitudes, the planet can be observed most easily in the evening in spring and in the morning in fall. At those times, Mercury's elongation from the Sun is greatest. This greatest elongation is merely 28 degrees.

Just like Venus and the Moon, Mercury has phases, waxing and waning from full to new Mercury. The planet travels on a path across the solar disc (called 'transit') approximately twelve times per century. A telescope would reveal Mercury as a small black disc in front of our huge central star. The next transit of Mercury will take place on November 8, 2006.

have high degrees of eccentricity; that is, they are more elliptical than those of the other planets.

The only planet with a stronger axial tilt is Pluto. Mercury rotates once about its axis in 59 Earth days. A Sun day, in other words the time span between two sunrises, is 176 Earth days. It takes Mercury 88 days to orbit the Sun.

Venus

Venus, the second planet in our solar system, is named after the goddess of love. For a long time, astronomers thought that life might have developed on Venus. Its mass and density, comparable to that of Earth, were arguments in favour of this notion. The planet's mass is 81.5 percent of Earth's. Its mean density is 5.25 grams per cubic centimetre. Furthermore, with a diameter of 12,150 kilometres, it is only slightly smaller than Earth. Venus also has an atmosphere full of thick clouds. Yet everything on the planet is incompatible with life. Below the closed cloud layer, temperatures of over 450 EC predominate. Heated by the Sun, the dense atmosphere prevents heat from escaping. This density is remarkable, and the pressure is comparable to the pressure at a depth of 1000 metres of water on Earth. The atmosphere consists of 95 % carbon dioxide. The mean distance from the Sun is 108 kilometres.

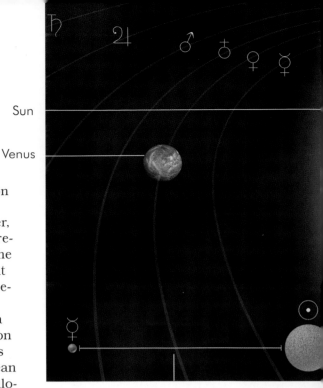

Sun

Venus

108,200,000 km

Orbit

Venus revolves around the Sun on an inner orbit as seen from the perspective of the Earth. One solar orbit takes 224.7 Earth days. During this orbit, the planet ends up between the Earth and the Sun. Consequently, like the Moon and Mercury, it is subject to different phases.

Venus's rotation is retrograde. It is very slow. One Venus day lasts longer than one Venus year. In other words, Venus revolves around the Sun faster than it rotates about its axis.

One Venus day is equivalent to 242 Earth days. Venus has a very small axial tilt (2.7 degrees) towards its orbital plane. The axial tilt of the Earth is much greater (23.5).

Atmosphere

The planet Venus is surrounded by a closed cloud layer. The upper regions of these clouds rotate once around the planet in only four days.

Sometimes, it even rains in this inhospitable environment, incompatible with any life. However, this rain consists of sulphuric acid. The raindrops never reach the surface. They evaporate in the enormous heat. Yet, despite these inhospitable conditions, space probes succeeded in landing on this planet and photographed its dusty surface.

Temperatures on Venus generally are over 450 EC. That is hot enough to melt lead. Practically all regions of Venus reach this temperature; only at the poles is it slightly cooler. This massive greenhouse effect turns Venus into the hottest planet in the solar system.

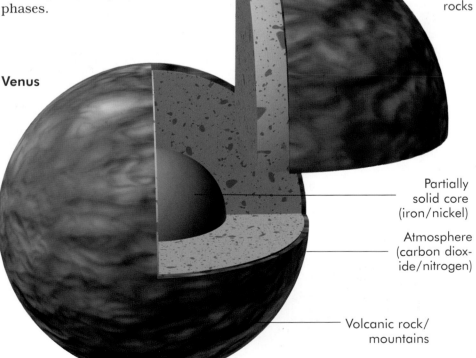

Venus

Crust/ rocks

Mantle/ rocks

Partially solid core (iron/nickel)

Atmosphere (carbon dioxide/nitrogen)

Volcanic rock/ mountains

While the Sun can warm the surface, the dense atmosphere of Venus with its enormous layers of haze prevents heat from being released. The pressure is 100 times that of air pressure on the Earth. The upper cloud layers rotate relatively quickly around the planet. Near the planet's surface, they are practically motionless. Because wind speed does not exceed a few kilometres per hour, there is no erosion. Thus, the surface remains essentially unchanged.

Surface

The surface of Venus consists of hot deserts, large plains, and a few mountains and valleys. The largest plateau is called Aphrodite Terra. It is located at the level of the Venus equator and is about as large as Africa.

All in all, Venus is less mountainous than Earth. There are some elevations that reach 11 kilometres in height (Maxwell Montes), but only 10 percent of the entire surface is mountainous. Much of the surface is taken up by large plains (70 percent) and lowlands (20 percent). Unlike Earth, the surface crust of Venus is a single plate. Aside from this, the two planets are similar in their structure. There is a core of liquid iron and nickel, a rocky mantle, and a thin outer rocky crust.

At least until 100 million years ago, Venus had a distinct pattern of volcanic eruptions. There possibly still are active volcanoes on the planet. Certainly, astronomers have discovered cooled off lava streams that are longer than the longest rivers on Earth. There are also craters on the surface of Venus, although far less than on Mercury. This is due to the fact that the dense atmosphere has deflected the entry of smaller celestial bodies. Larger chunks of rock, however, have reached the surface, leaving impact craters in their wake. Given the limited amount of erosion on Venus, these craters have remained intact.

Observing Venus/ Venus Phases

Venus is one of the inner planets. The orbit passes between the Sun and Earth's orbit. Like the moon, Venus is subject to different observable phases.

During the phases of the waning or waxing Venus crescent, the planet can be observed particularly well. At the time of inferior or superior conjunction, the planet is invisible to us. Conjunction means that various celestial bodies are located along the same longitude. During the inferior conjunction (sequence Earth–Venus–Sun), Venus is at its closest to Earth. Since Venus's night side is turned towards us, we cannot see the planet. Then Venus begins to wax, eventually reaching the point of greatest distance. If the planet is to the right of the Sun, in other words, during the waxing phase, it is referred to as the morning star. During the waning phase, Venus is referred to as the evening star. The greater the elongation of Venus from the Sun, the easier it is to observe the planet. The greatest elongation is 48 degrees. Mercury's greatest elongation is only 28 degrees. As a result of this difference, Venus can be seen for a longer period of time after sundown and earlier before sunrise than Mercury.

Just like Mercury, Venus moves around the Sun on an orbit inside the orbit of Earth. Like Mercury, this planet has a pattern of waning and waxing crescent shapes. If Venus is behind the Sun, i.e., when the Sun is between the planet and Earth, one describes this as an upper conjunction. When Venus has reached a point between Earth and Sun during its orbit, this is referred to as lower conjunction.

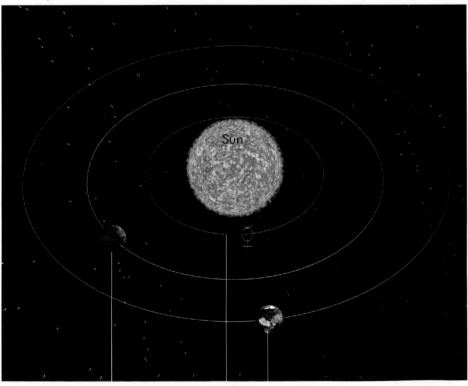

Venus   Mercury's orbit   Earth

Mars

Our outer neighbour in the planetary system is the planet most like Earth. Mars was named after the Roman god of war (Greek: Ares). This has inspired science fiction authors to populate their novels with fictive Martians, invariably depicted as a warlike people. Again and again, humans suffer attacks by evil Martians. But could life actually have developed on Mars? The American astronomer Percival Lowell was a proponent of this idea. He argued that the faults and de-

pressions (canali) on the surface of the planet, discovered by the astronomer Giovanni Schiaparelli as early as 1877, are part of an artificial irrigation system.

In 1976, Viking space probes showed that higher life forms could not have developed on Mars. Even the "canali" were shown to be optical illusions. It is not entirely impossible that there might have been simple life forms, which might perhaps still be hidden inside lower aqueous layers, but it is not very likely.

Mars is about half the size of the Earth. A Martian day is only 40 minutes longer than an Earth day. There also are seasons; however, these seasons are twice as long as seasons on Earth. The maximum distance from the Earth is approximately 400 million kilometres. When the planets are opposite one another, the distance

Mars

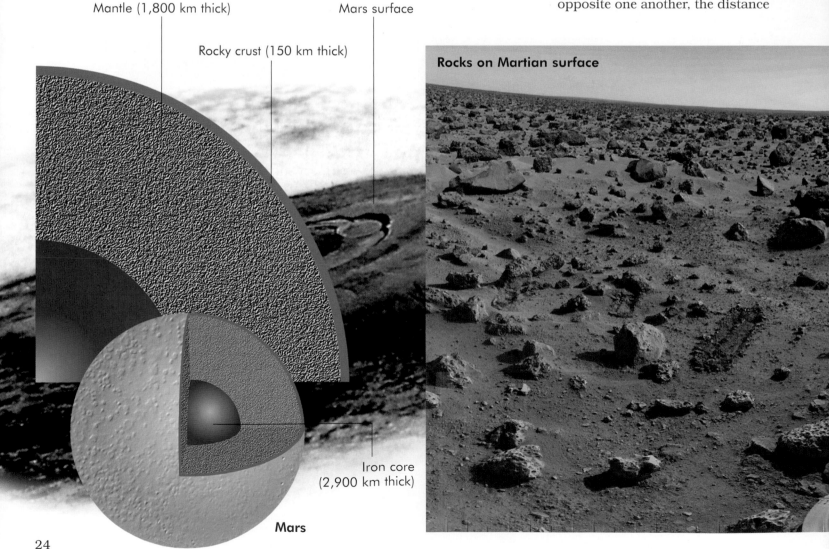

Mantle (1,800 km thick)

Rocky crust (150 km thick)

Mars surface

Iron core (2,900 km thick)

Rocks on Martian surface

Mars

between them shrinks to 55.65 million kilometres. It takes Mars approximately two years to orbit the Sun. It is significantly colder on Mars than on Earth. The average temperature is –25 EC, and temperatures range from +20 EC to –120 EC. Due to limited gravity, the atmosphere is very thin. Consequently, it cannot absorb and store the Sun's heat and instead releases it very quickly.

This thin atmosphere consists of 95 % carbon dioxide. The characteristic red colouration of the planet is caused by aqueous iron oxide in the surface dust. One might say that Mars is rusty.

Orbit

Mars, the fourth planet from the Sun, is our outer neighbour. Its orbit is not parallel to the orbit of Earth. That means that there are considerable fluctuations in the distance between Mars and Earth. They are in closest proximity when they are in opposition. This happens when the Sun, the Earth and Mars form a line.

Mars' orbit is more elliptical than circular. That means that there is a great deal of variation in distance during opposition. During opposition at the point of greatest distance from the Sun, known as aphelion, most recently on 12 February 1995, the distance between Mars and Earth was approximately 101 million kilometres. During the most recent opposition at the point of shortest

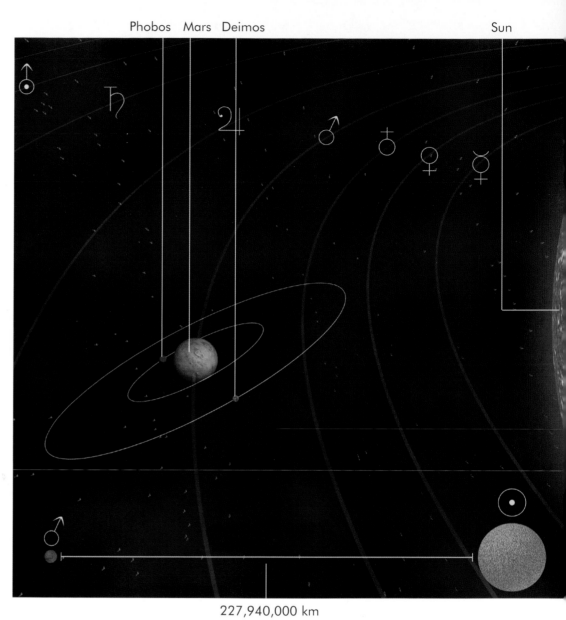

227,940,000 km

Mars is the outermost of the planets most like Earth. One Mars day is only slightly longer than an Earth day: 24 hours and 37 minutes. Mars has two moons, Phobos and Deimos. Each has a diameter of just a few kilometres and they revolve around the planet on their own orbits.

distance from the Sun on 28 August 2003, known as perihelion, the distance between the planets was "only" 55.8 million kilometres. The next opposition is on 7 November 2005. When Mars and Earth are in conjunction, that is, situated across from each other, they are at the greatest distance from each other. At those times, when the Sun is between the planets, there is a distance of 400 million kilometres between Mars and Earth. Mars needs

almost two years to orbit the Sun (687 days). Observation of Mars over a longer period of time shows an apparent looping motion. Mars does not appear to follow its orbit, but instead appears to stop and even reverse itself. This phenomenon is due to the different orbital speeds of Mars and Earth. In opposition, the inner planet (Earth) passes the outer planet (Mars), because that planet has to travel a greater distance.

Mars has a small hard core and a silicate rock mantle. The adjoining hard crust is surrounded by a thin atmosphere consisting for the most part of carbon dioxide. On the rust-coloured surface we can observe mountains and ravines as well as many craters and impact basins.

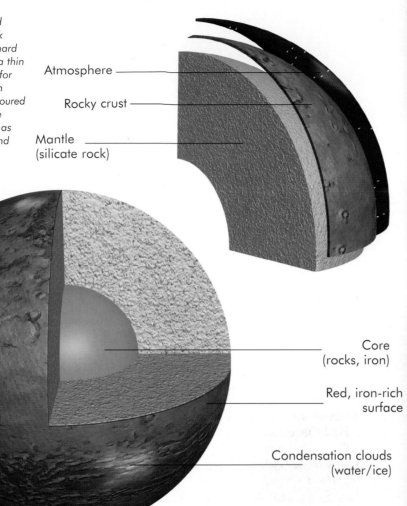

Atmosphere

Rocky crust

Mantle
(silicate rock)

Core
(rocks, iron)

Red, iron-rich
surface

Condensation clouds
(water/ice)

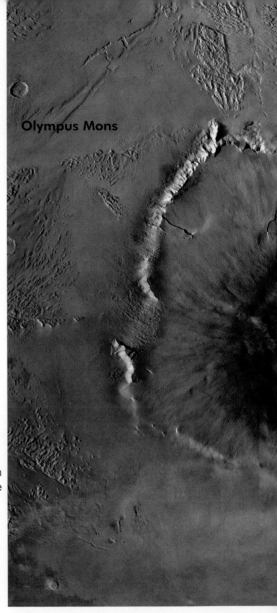

Olympus Mons

Surface

The most noticeable characteristic of the Martian surface is its reddish tint. This is caused by iron oxidation in the rocky sediment and dust. The planet is "rusty".

Mars has very diverse landscapes. In addition to crater-pocked plains and mountains, there are huge deserts, icy polar caps, deep faults and high volcanoes.

The craters were caused by meteorites, but unlike the craters on Venus, the Martian craters are partially eroded. This is due to strong winds that in some instances can turn into powerful storms. These winds stir up the dust, so that the thin Martian atmosphere has a reddish tint. Sand storms can continue for months, sometimes, as in 1971, enveloping the entire planet. However, the erosion is not as pronounced as it is on the Earth. Also, there are no continental plates that can collide or drift apart. The Martian crust consists of a single plate. This facilitated the formation of very high volcanoes. The giant of these volcanoes is Olympus Mons. It is the highest mountain in the solar system. Its diameter is 600 kilometres, and it reaches a height of 27 kilometres, about three times as large as Mount Everest. The dimensions of some ravines are remarkable as well. Near the equator there is a huge plain, the so-called Valles Marineres. It contains ravines that are four times

Ice caps on Mars

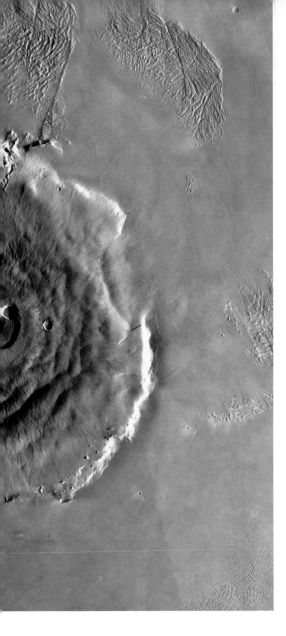

Moons

Mars has two satellites. They were named after the two companions of Mars, Deimos and Phobos, 'Terror' and 'Fear'. Asaph Hall discovered them in 1877. Their peculiar shape earned the satellites the nickname 'potato moons'. Their appearance suggests that they originated in the planetoid belt and were captured by Mars. Deimos has a diameter of 12 kilometres. Its dark rock has only a few craters and its surface is smoother than that of Phobos. Its mean distance to Mars is 23,500 kilometres, corresponding to a 30-hour orbital period. Phobos is the more interesting of the two. With a diameter of 20 kilometres, it is larger than Deimos. It orbits Mars in a mere 7 hours and 40 minutes. For this reason, it looks as if the moon were running backwards.

Phobos is literally littered with craters. The largest of these, called Stickney, has a diameter of 10 kilometres. Eventually, however, Phobos will itself create a crater. Its fate can be predicted: moving closer and closer to the surface of Mars, the moon will finally hit the planet 50 to 100 million years from now.

Rotation

A Martian day has 24 hours and 37 minutes. That is how long it takes for the planet to rotate about its axis. The rotational axis is tilted 24 degrees towards the orbital plane. An axial tilt, comparable to that of Earth, but more pronounced by 1.7 degrees, causes the seasons. During a given season, certain areas are turned more towards the Sun and others are turned away.

Given the longer orbit of Mars, twice as long as that of Earth, seasons are also twice as long. It takes Mars 687 Earth days (= 1 Mars year) to orbit the Sun.

as deep and ten times as long as the Grand Canyon.

Astronomers also discovered that the weather on Mars changes. Just as on Earth, there are various cloud formations. One can also observe seasons. In summer, temperatures on Mars rise above +10EC.

The ice on the south pole disappears almost entirely. There is no water in liquid form on Mars, however, although dried up riverbeds lead us to conclude that there was water at one time. Today there are probably only some permafrost layers left in Martian soil, comparable to what one would find in our tundras.

Deimos

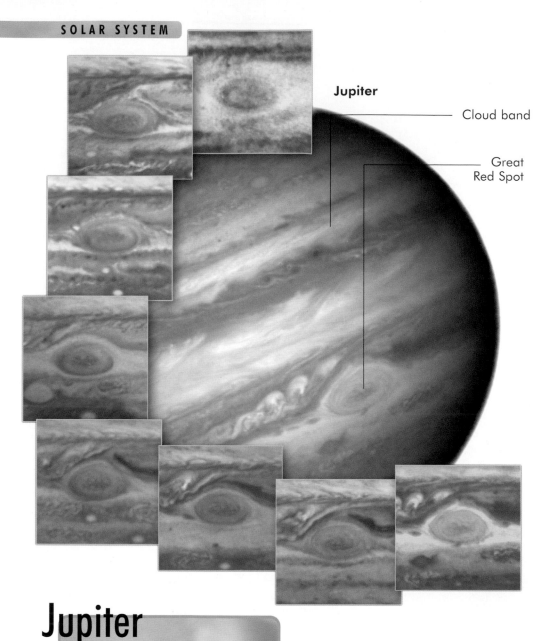

Jupiter

— Cloud band

— Great
Red Spot

Jupiter

Jupiter is the giant in the solar system, accounting for 70 percent of the total mass of all planets. We can only see its dense atmosphere, which is eight times as thick as that of Earth.

Closer towards its core, there is a layer of liquid hydrogen. Crystallization, a consequence of enormous pressure, transforms this layer into metallic hydrogen. In the upper cloud layers, temperatures drop down to –150 EC. Jupiter radiates 1.7 times more energy than it receives from the Sun. However, this giant planet could not become a sun. Despite its size, it does not have the critical mass

required for the process of nuclear energy creation.

Jupiter is not only the largest, but also the fastest planet. It needs less than 10 hours for a complete rotation about its axis. This tremendous rotational velocity in turn affects the cloud structures. Cloud bands are formed, which orbit the planet in zones. Astronomers distinguish approximately 10 zones, broken down by the northern and the southern hemisphere (temperate, tropical and equatorial). The individual cloud zones rush around the planet at speeds of up to 500 kilometres per hour. These

zones appear to be stable and long-lived. Since more intensive observation of the planet has become possible, i.e., approximately for the last 50 years, the structures have hardly changed at all.

The rotational velocity also helps to ensure that Jupiter has a distinctive magnetic field. The magnetic field's rays expand across 90 Jupiter radiuses, reaching even across the orbit of Saturn. Radiation is 10,000 times as intense as that of the magnetic field of Earth. Astronomers enjoyed a remarkable spectacle in July 1994. The comet Shoemaker-Levy 9 broke up, and its fragments crashed onto the planet. The brightness of the tremendous explosions caused by the collision exceeded Jupiter's brightness by more than 50 times.

Great Red Spot

The phenomenon of the Great Red Spot is apparent on practically every photograph of Jupiter ever published. It is the largest and longest-lived storm in the solar system. To be precise, it is an anticyclical hurricane.

It protrudes above the cloud layer by more than 8 kilometres. The diameter of the Great Red Spot is three times as large as that of Earth. This super storm was already discovered 300 years ago, albeit without anyone understanding what it signified. Since that time, the storm has been drawn repeatedly and later photographed, and it has been demonstrated that it occasionally changes size.

The colour is due to phosphor, created when turbulent gases in the upper atmospheric layer react to the sunlight. The Great Red Spot rotates once about its axis approximately every ten days. It also orbits the planet. However, this is a slow journey, taking place at varying speeds.

How could such a tremendous hurricane continue to exist for such a long time? Unlike Earth, Jupiter provides the conditions for immediate recycling of clouds. On Earth, clouds are created gradually in the course of evaporation. After they have turned into rain, it takes some time before new clouds are formed. On Jupiter, however, rain comes down into an extremely hot atmosphere and evaporates immediately.

Jupiter, the largest of all the planets, orbits the Sun in 9 hours and 55 minutes. It has sixteen moons that orbit the planet in three groups. The four outer moons orbit the planet in the opposite direction from the inner moons. They are at a distance of more than 20,000 million kilometres from the centre of Jupiter.

778,330,000 km

Orbit

Jupiter orbits the sun in approximately 11.86 Earth years. The mean distance from the Sun is 778 million kilometres. Its orbital speed is 13.05 kilometres per second. In comparison, Earth orbits the Sun at a speed of nearly 30 kilometres per second. The giant planet's rotational velocity (one rotation about its axis = one day) is greater than that of Earth, indeed greater than that of any other planet. Our day is 24 hours long; a day on Jupiter is no more than 9 hours and 55 minutes. That means that, under the right conditions, one might be able to observe a complete Jupiter day over the course of one night on Earth. The rotational axis is tilted only slightly (orbital inclination of 3.1 degrees). Earth's axis is noticeably more tilted (23.4 degrees). Another consequence of Jupiter's rotational velocity is that the equator bulges outward.

Structure

Jupiter, a hydrogen gas giant, is so huge that it could accommodate Earth 1,300 times. The equatorial diameter is 143,000 kilometres. At the centre of the planet is a rocky core, with a diameter of approximately 25,000 kilometres and temperatures of up to 30,000 EC. This core is surrounded by a layer of metallic hydrogen. In conjunction with the rotational velocity, this layer helps to create the distinctive magnetic field of the planet. The layer of metallic hydrogen merges into a wide belt of liquid hydrogen. This in turn merges into the atmospheric layer, which consists of 90 percent hydrogen, 10 percent helium, and traces of other substances such as ammonia, methane and steam. Another substance is phosphine, a flammable gas notable for its garlicky odour.

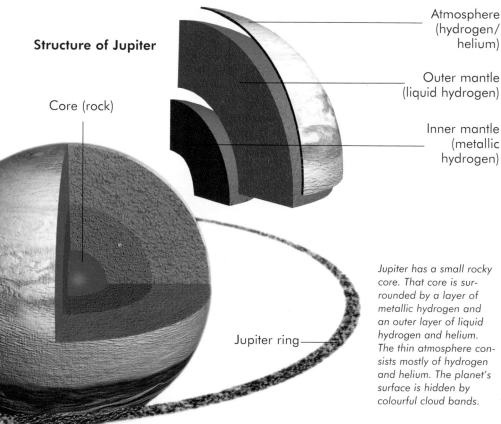

Structure of Jupiter

Core (rock)

Atmosphere (hydrogen/helium)

Outer mantle (liquid hydrogen)

Inner mantle (metallic hydrogen)

Jupiter ring

Jupiter has a small rocky core. That core is surrounded by a layer of metallic hydrogen and an outer layer of liquid hydrogen and helium. The thin atmosphere consists mostly of hydrogen and helium. The planet's surface is hidden by colourful cloud bands.

Moons

Jupiter has one ring and 16 moons. The four largest are called Galileo moons, since he first discovered them. Their names are Io, Europa, Ganymede and Callisto.

All moons are located outside the ring. The first moons along the main ring are Adrastea and Metis, followed by Amalthea and Thebe. These are followed by the four Galileo moons. The next ones are Leda, Himalia, Lysithea and Elara. The four moons farthest from Jupiter are called Ananke, Carme, Pasiphae and Sinope. These moons, which orbit their planet in the opposite direction, most likely are trapped planetoids from the asteroid belt. They orbit Jupiter at a distance of up to 24 million kilometres. While the four Galileo moons are larger than our Moon, the other 12 are rather small. None of them has a diameter of more than 200 kilometres.

The Galileo moons are interesting for other reasons as well. Io is distinctively red and yellow. This is due to volcanoes that spew forth sulphur. Io's exposure to Jupiter's magnetic field results in two powerful electrical currents between the two. Io's volcanoes are the most active in the solar system. It has a diameter of 3,640 kilometres, and it is at a distance of 422,000 kilometres from Jupiter.

Like Io, Europa is one of the younger moons. The space probe Galileo photographed Europa in

Sulphur volcano

Jupiter's moon Io

Volcano

Io

Io is one of the most active moons in our solar system. Powerful active volcanoes, affected by the tides of Jupiter, spew enormous amounts of sulphur into Io's atmosphere.

1997. This revealed surprising facts: this moon has an ocean on which icebergs are floating. Until that point time, it had been generally accepted that the discovery of liquid water on celestial bodies other than Earth was highly unlikely. The low age of the moon is confirmed by the limited number of meteorite craters. Europa has a diameter of 3,140 kilometres. Its distance from Jupiter is 671,000 kilometres.

Ganymede is the largest moon in the solar system. Its diameter of 5,262 kilometres is noticeably larger than that of Mercury. Its distance to Jupiter is 1,070,000 kilometres. Ganymede has an icy crater-pocked crust.

The outermost of the four Galileo moons is Callisto. Its surface is also

riddled with craters. The most impressive of these is Valhalla, spanning 300 kilometres. It takes Callisto 17 days to orbit Jupiter. Its distance from Jupiter is 1.9 million kilometres. The fourth Galileo Moon is almost as large as Mercury (4,880 kilometres).

In 1980, the spacecraft Voyager I discovered that Jupiter has rings. The main ring is approximately 30 kilometres thick and 6,500 kilometres wide. This faint structure, hovering 50,000 to 58,000 kilometres above the planet's cloud layer, consists of fine dust. An even finer halo ring reaches as far as the cloud layer.

Saturn

Saturn is known as the "Lord of the Rings". It is one of the four giant planets and the sixth planet from the Sun. Its ring system is without a doubt its most notable characteristic. Galileo had basically discovered it in 1610. However, since the telescopes at his disposal were not strong enough, he decided that it was a moon. In 1656, the Dutch astronomer Huygens realized that in fact this celestial apparition consisted of rings. Saturn is twice as far from the Sun as Jupiter. When observing Saturn from the Earth, you need excellent optical instruments in order to be able to recognize the rings, which consist of thousands of millions of ice and rock fragments.

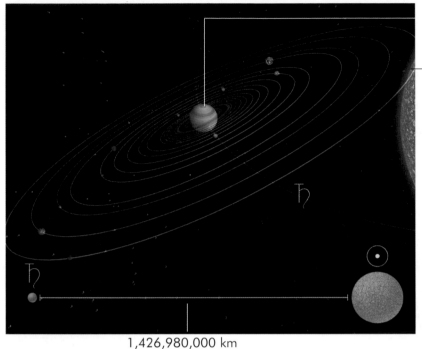

Saturn with rings and moons

Sun

While rotating rapidly, Saturn orbits the Sun along with its ring system and moons, 18 of which have been discovered thus far. These can be divided into small groups sharing the same orbit. The outermost moon, Phoebe, orbits in the opposite direction from the others.

1,426,980,000 km

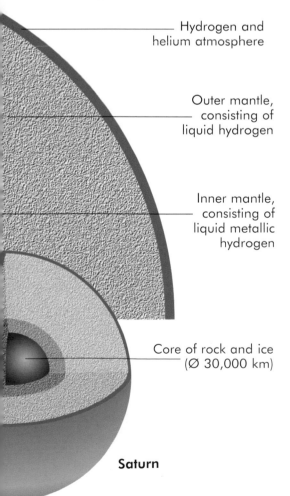

Hydrogen and helium atmosphere

Outer mantle, consisting of liquid hydrogen

Inner mantle, consisting of liquid metallic hydrogen

Core of rock and ice (Ø 30,000 km)

Saturn

There is a noticeable gap between the rings. The French astrologer Jean-Dominique Cassini, born in Italy, discovered this gap, which was then named after him (Cassini Division). The Saturn space probe Cassini, sent into space in October 1997, was also named after him. A particular task for the Cassini space probe was the exploration of Saturn's moon, Titan.

On Saturn, day has approximately 10 hours and 25 minutes. Its great rotational velocity brings about a flattening along the poles and a bulging out along the equator. The equatorial diameter is 120,500 kilo-metres, while the polar diameter is 108,800 kilometres.

Because the layer of metallic hydrogen is relatively thin (compared to Jupiter), the high rotational velocity does not have much of an effect on the magnetic field. The temperature in this turbulent atmosphere is –180 EC. Like Jupiter, Saturn radiates more energy than it receives from the Sun. Its mass is 95 times the mass of Earth. However, its density is less than that of water. This means that it is the only planet in the solar system that would float.

Orbit

One Saturn year is the equivalent of 29 Earth years and 167 days. In this time span, the planet orbits the Sun at a distance ranging from 1.35 to 1.5 thousand million kilo-metres. The rotational velocity is slightly lower than that of Jupiter, but, at 10 hours and 25 minutes, is still quite fast. Just as in the case of Earth, Saturn's rotational axis is tilted. The tilt of the equator towards the orbital plane is approximately 27 degrees. Since the planet's rings are tilted accordingly, they can be observed from Earth in various positions. At two times during a Saturn year, the rings can barely be seen, because we are looking directly at their edge. A maximum opening of the rings could be observed in 2003.

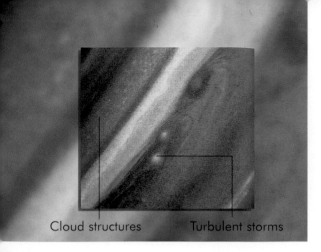

Cloud structures Turbulent storms

Surface

Saturn has a core of rocks and ice with a diameter of approximately 30,000 kilometres. The next layer consists of metallic hydrogen. Since this layer is not as thick as that of Jupiter, and since the rotational velocity is lower, the magnetic field is 20 times smaller than that of its neighbour. The main part of the planet is taken up by a layer of liquid hydrogen, located in the outer mantle. Cloud bands travel around the planet on a plane parallel to the equator. Sometimes hurricanes develop, as is the case with the Great Red Spot on Jupiter. But these storms are minor and not long-lived. They are more pronounced in the vicinity of the equator, where wind speeds of up to 2,000 kilometres per hour can be reached.

The main components of the atmosphere are hydrogen and helium. These light elements have a low density of only 0.69 grams per cubic metre. Consequently, Saturn is the only planet with a density less than that of water.

Ring System

Saturn is not the only planet with a ring system. The three other large planets (Jupiter, Uranus and Neptune) also have ring systems; however, none are as complex or impressive as the Saturnian rings. Three rings can be seen from Earth. The A ring is the outermost of these visible rings. Inside of it is a small gap where there are interior moons. The B ring has dark spokes. That means that matter is not evenly distributed along the ring. Presumably, this is due to dust clouds that are affected by electrical fields. The faintest ring that can be seen from Earth is the C ring. This ring, like the others, consists of many individual bands. Four other ring groups (D–G) have been discovered by space probes. The faint E ring consists of very fine particles. It has the greatest expanse. Portions of the F ring are like braids or ringlets.

There also is the barely noticeable G ring and the innermost D ring that extends almost to Saturn's atmosphere. Despite their huge dimensions, the total mass of the rings is limited, no more than approximately 1/25,000 of the mass of Saturn. The individual particles of which the ring system is composed consist of rocks and ice. Presumably, at some point at the dawn of time, a moon came too close to the planet and was ground to bits by the strong gravitational pull. In 1675, Cassini discovered a gap between the A ring and the B ring. Thanks to photographs taken by the space probe Voyager, we now know that the Cassini Division is not entirely empty. Several dozen narrow rings consisting of fine dust particles were found in this opening, which is approximately 4,000 kilometres wide. The individual components of these rings range from particles of microscopic dimensions to blocks with a diameter of up to 10 metres.

Moons

Saturn's moon Enceladus

No other planet has as many satellites as Saturn. We do not know their exact number. Currently, we are aware of as many as 18 moons, but astronomers believe that there may well be several more. The moons orbit Saturn in groups; in other words, several travel along a single orbit. It is likely that these were part of a common celestial body at another point in time. The outermost Saturn moon is Phoebe, located at a distance of 13 million kilometres from its parent planet. It orbits Saturn in the opposite direction and presumably is a trapped planetoid.

The largest of Saturn's moons is Titan, with a diameter of approximately 5,150 kilometres. It is only slightly smaller than the largest moon in the solar system, Ganymede. It is the only moon with a dense atmosphere. This characteristic makes Titan an especially interesting object of exploration. The space probe Cassini set off into space in October 1997. On 14 January 2005, the Cassini orbiter released the space probe Huygens into Titan's atmosphere. Huygens was developed by the European Space Agency (ESA). The space probe is expected to help gain more insight into the origins of the atmosphere on Earth. We still know relatively little about the surface of Titan. It is possible that we will find oceans and icebergs consisting of methane. The temperature on Titan is extremely low, presumably less than −160 EC. It is even colder on Enceladus. On this very bright, ice-covered moon it is −200 EC. The Voyager research programme helped bring to light interesting details about several other moons. For instance, on the moon Mimas, less than 400 kilo-

metres in diameter, an impact crater takes up a third of the moon's diameter. The icy moon Tethys has a system of canyons (Ithaca Chasm) with a length of more than 2,000 kilometres and a crater (Odysseus) that is 400 kilometres wide. The moons Dione and Rhea, 1,100 and 1,500 kilometres in diameter respectively, have only a few craters, but these are very large. The inner moons help to create a clearly defined barrier for the Saturn rings. Portions of the F ring even look as if they were braided. This is due to the gravitational force of the sheepdog moons Pandora and Prometheus. They earned this name

Titan

because they guard the ring particles and keep them together just as a dog guards and herds his sheep. The moons Epimetheus and Janus, presumably united at one time, trade orbits every four years. Calypso and Telesto travel along the same orbit as Tethys, one 60 degrees ahead, the other 60 degrees behind. The so-called Trojans, planetoids in Jupiter's orbit, are also known for this phenomenon. The moon Helene is on the same orbit as Dione. It is very curious that the hemispheres of the moon Iapetus differ in their degree of brightness.

Uranus

Uranus

The planet Uranus is twice as far away from the Sun as Saturn. Discovered by Herschel in 1781, this planet is the seventh in our solar system. Given the great mean distance from the Sun, only a small portion of light arrives at the planet. One result of this is that it is ex-

ceedingly cold on Uranus, with a temperature of −215 EC. Its structure is similar to that of Jupiter and Saturn.

The atmosphere consists mostly of hydrogen (83 percent), with small portions of helium (15 percent)

and methane (2 percent). By the mid-1980s, astronomers knew of five moons.

Voyager 2 discovered another ten moons, admittedly much smaller. The moons were named after characters from various Shakespeare plays.

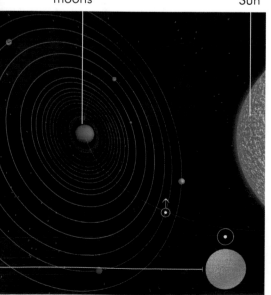

Uranus with moons   Sun

Orbit

It takes Uranus 84 years (= 1 Uranus year) to orbit the Sun. It rotates about its axis in 17 hours and 15 minutes (= 1 Uranus day). The mean distance from the Sun is 2.88 thousand million kilometres. Uranus travels along its orbit at a speed of 6.81 kilometres per second. Its axial tilt towards the perpendicular line of the orbital plane is extraordinary. At 98 degrees of orbital inclination, this axial tilt is far greater than that of any other planet (as a comparison,

Uranus orbits the Sun with an extreme axial tilt. It has 11 rings with dust planes in between.

one might consider Earth's orbital inclination of 23.5 degrees). This means that the planet is practically reclining on its orbital plane, while alternately turning its southern hemisphere and its northern hemisphere towards the Sun. Thus, winter and summer in the northern hemisphere each last 42 years. However, due to the great distance from the Sun, the difference in temperature between the seasons is minimal, no more than 2 EC. Uranus has a ring system, which, however, is not very developed. The 15 moons known to date revolve around Uranus on their own orbits, some of which are located inside and others outside this ring system.

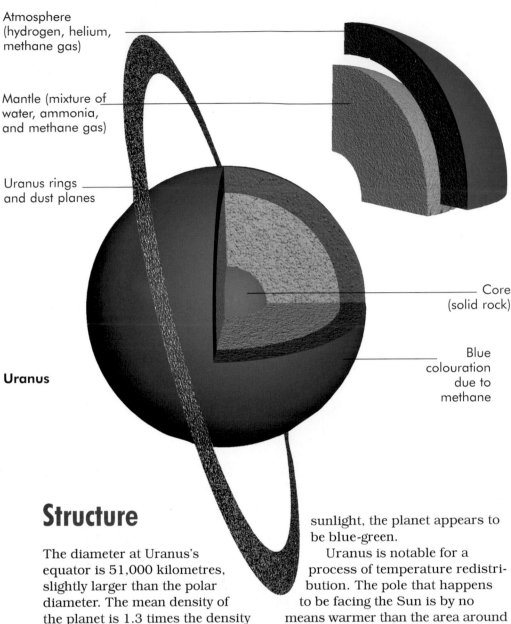

Atmosphere
(hydrogen, helium,
methane gas)

Mantle (mixture of
water, ammonia,
and methane gas)

Uranus rings
and dust planes

Uranus

Core
(solid rock)

Blue
colouration
due to
methane

Structure

The diameter at Uranus's equator is 51,000 kilometres, slightly larger than the polar diameter. The mean density of the planet is 1.3 times the density of water. Hence, its density is greater than that of Saturn and Jupiter. From this, it is reasonable to conclude that Uranus must have more heavy elements than the other planets.

The structure is similar to that of its inner neighbours, but there are some differences. In the centre of the planet is a rocky core. This 7,000 EC core is enclosed in a layer that consists of a mixture of water, methane and ammonia. This layer merges into the atmospheric layer of hydrogen, helium and methane. Since methane gas absorbs red

sunlight, the planet appears to be blue-green.

Uranus is notable for a process of temperature redistribution. The pole that happens to be facing the Sun is by no means warmer than the area around the equator, which is hardly exposed to sunlight at all. In this area, the winds are strongest, reaching velocities of up to 1,000 kilometres per hour. The surface is essentially without a defined structure. Voyager 2 discovered only a few thin cloud bands during its flight past the planet in 1986. It was astonishing that the clouds did not move in the expected direction. The strong axial tilt had led astronomers to assume that winds would move from north to south. In fact, however, they move along the equatorial plane.

Moons

Uranus has fifteen satellites and a ring system. The five larger moons have been known for some time. The other ten moons and a ring were discovered only in 1986 by the space probe Voyager 2.

Just like the rings, the moons are located on a plane above the equator.

William Herschel discovered Titania and Oberon in 1787. These two moons radiate the most light.

In the mid 19th century, astronomers discovered Ariel and Umbriel. Finally, Miranda was discovered in 1948.

The moons that were discovered first are located farthest away from the planet.

Oberon is located at a distance of 580,000 kilometres. The next closest to the planet is Titania, the largest of Uranus's moons (with a diameter of 1,580 kilometres), consisting of rock and ice. Its surface has deep grooves. Umbriel's surface is darker. The next moons are Ariel and Miranda, the smallest of the moons.

The names of the smaller satellites also are derived from various Shakespeare plays – Puck, Belinda, Rosalind, Portia, Juliet, Desdemona, Cressida, Bianca, Ophelia and Cordelia. Ophelia and Cordelia are known as sheepdog moons. Cordelia is located inside the ring system. These small moons are essentially large clumps of rock and ice. None of them has a diameter that exceeds 150 kilometres. They are not massive enough to develop the typical spherical shape of a moon.

Neptune

Great
Dark Spot

'Scooter'

Neptune

The cold and windy planet Neptune is the eighth planet in our solar system. Its coordinates were calculated and predicted before the planet had even been discovered. Astronomers knew that Uranus tended to deviate slightly from its orbit. In the mid-19th century, the British astronomer John Couch Adams and the French astronomer Urbain Leverrier concluded that another celestial body had to cause this orbital shift. In 1846, the German astronomer Johann Galle succeeded in sighting the missing planet in the previously calculated location. However, we had to wait until the explorations of Voyager 2 in 1989 to learn more about the planet. The diameter of its equator is just under 50,000 kilometres. In contrast to Uranus, there are clearly recognizable structures in the planet's atmosphere. One of these is a well-developed storm system – large enough to accommodate the entire planet Earth. Wind speeds in this storm system reach more than 2,000 kilometres per hour. Given the density of Neptune's atmosphere, wind travels practically as fast as the speed of sound. This also means that Neptune is the stormiest planet in our solar system. Neptune radiates 2.5 times as much heat as it receives from the Sun in the form of energy. It is also the fourth planet with a ring system. Neptune has eight moons; one of these, Triton, can well be described as the coldest place in our solar system.

Neptune — Atmosphere (hydrogen, helium, methane gas); Mantle (water ice, ammonia ice, and methane ice); Rocky core

Orbit

Neptune orbits the Sun at a mean distance of 4.5 thousand million kilometres. This is the equivalent of 30 astronomical units (AU). An astronomical unit is based on the mean distance between the Sun and the Earth. The planet completes its enormous orbit around the Sun in 165.5 years (= 1 Neptune year). Its rotational period, or one Neptune day, is 16 hours and 7 minutes. However, it is not possible to determine this time value on the basis of observation, since the atmospheric structures do not offer a fixed point of reference.

Neptune with moons — Sun

Neptune orbits the Sun with an orbital tilt similar to that of Earth. It is surrounded by a ring system and has 8 moons, each with its own orbit. The outermost moon, Nereid, at a distance of 5.5 million kilometres, revolves in the opposite direction from the other moons.

Structure

Neptune's structure is comparable to that of Uranus. While smaller than Uranus, the planet has a greater density, which leads to the conclusion that the hot rocky core is more powerful as well. Consideration of some figures helps to illustrate this point: assuming a value of 1 for water, Uranus would have a density of 1.3 and Neptune 1.65. The core is enclosed in a mantle of hydrogen, ammonia and methane.

This layer merges into the atmospheric layer. Its components are above all hydrogen (85 percent) and helium (13 percent). Methane is also present, which causes the blue colouration of the planet. The atmosphere of Neptune contains more recognizable structures than the atmosphere of Uranus. Most notable is the Great Dark Spot, located south

4,497,070,000 km

of the equator. If one takes into account Jupiter's size, the dimensions of Neptune's spot are comparable to that of the Great Red Spot. It also is a storm system. The hurricane on Neptune, however, is faster, reaching speeds of approximately 2,200 kilometres per hour. This is the windiest corner in the solar system. The upper layers of the atmosphere contain white methane ice clouds. Since the clouds throw shadows, they must be quite high in the atmosphere. Near the south pole is another storm, referred to as the Small Dark Spot or Scooter. The two storm areas orbit the planet in opposite directions. A hazy mist of hydrocarbon elements is located above the atmosphere.

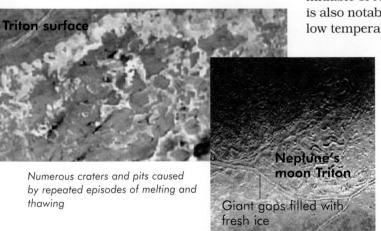

Triton surface

Numerous craters and pits caused by repeated episodes of melting and thawing

Neptune's moon Triton

Giant gaps filled with fresh ice

Moons

Neptune has eight satellites. Four of these are inside and four outside the ring system. Naiad and Thalassa, two so-called sheepdog moons, are located inside the ring system. These are followed by Despoina and Galatea. The first moon outside the rings is Larissa. The next one is Proteus, located at a distance of 118,000 kilometres from the parent planet. It has a diameter of 400 kilometres, and its surface is riddled with craters.

Triton orbits Neptune at a distance of approximately 355,000 kilometres. It is the only large moon that orbits its parent planet in the opposite direction. With a diameter of 2,760 kilometres, it is the most formidable of Neptune's satellites. It is also notable for its unbelievably low temperatures. At –235 EC, it is closer to the absolute zero point of –273 EC (0 degrees Kelvin) than any other body in the solar system. While Triton's northern tip has a blue shimmer, the south pole looks pink. On the southern hemisphere there are ice volcanoes that spew forth nitrogen

steam and dust. Nereid has the longest orbit. Its distance to Neptune is 5.5 million kilometres. Nereid has a diameter of no more than 250 kilometres, but is one of the two moons that we have already known about for a longer period of time. The others were discovered by Voyager 2.

It is possible that there are other sheepdog moons inside the rings. The smaller satellites are relatively faint and consist of rocks and ice. Neptune has two narrow and two broad rings. They are weakly defined and consist of ice for the most part. In the outer narrow ring there are a few bulges, also described as larger bodies. This is an unusual circumstance. Normally, matter is distributed evenly on the ring plane. However, the total mass of the four rings is so small that it would be barely sufficient for one small moon.

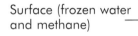

Surface (frozen water and methane)

Icy mantle

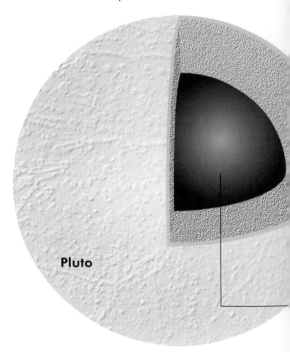

Pluto

Pluto

Pluto is the outermost planet in our solar system. Its mean distance from the Sun is almost 6 thousand million kilometres. It does not have any rings, and it has only one satellite, Charon. With a diameter of 2,300 kilometres, it is the smallest planet, even smaller than some moons. Just as happened with Neptune, Pluto's orbit

was calculated before the planet itself could be discovered. The American astronomer Tombaugh discovered it in 1930. It is most likely that Pluto consists of rock and ice. Its surface temperature is –220 EC. One day, or one rotational period, is 6.4 Earth days. Pluto's mean density is twice that of water.

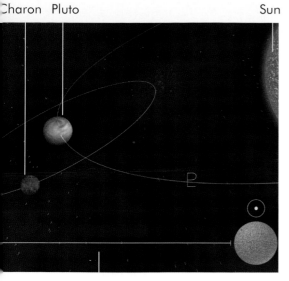

Charon Pluto · · · · · Sun

5,913,520,000 km

Pluto needs 248.4 years to complete one solar orbit, travelling on its very elliptical orbit. Its moon Charon is half its size. For this reason, the two are often described as a double planet system.

Orbit

It takes Pluto 248.4 years to complete one orbit around the Sun. Its orbit is unique, the most eccentric of all the orbits. It is so elliptical that there is a tremendous difference between the greatest and shortest distance from the Sun (7.38 thousand million and 4.4 thousand million kilometres respectively). Furthermore, the orbital inclination is much higher than that of the other planets, tilted 17 degrees in comparison to the ecliptic plane. As a result of these irregularities, Pluto is not always the outermost planet. Within a given 248-year period, the planet intersects with Neptune's orbit over a time span of approximately 20 years. The most recent twenty-year time span began in the spring of 1999.

——— Core (rock and possibly also ice)

Charon

In concert with Pluto, Charon acts like a double planet. They orbit a common centre of gravity that is located between the two celestial bodies.

Their powerful effect on each other is due to the relatively limited distance of less than 20,000 kilometres. Furthermore, Charon is the largest moon in the solar system in terms of its relative size vis-à-vis the parent planet. With a diameter of approximately 1,200 kilometres, it is half the size of Pluto (1:2). In comparison, one might consider the proportional relationship of Earth and Moon (1:4). While Pluto rotates about its axis in a period of 6.4 days, Charon orbits its partner in the same time. For this reason, two areas on Pluto and Charon are always directly opposite from each other. From the perspective of the planet, the far side of its moon is never visible. Charon's surface is presumably more defined than that of its parent planet. It consists of very solid ice. Given the limited mass, there is no methane ice as there is on Pluto. Charon's surface is also darker. Most of these discoveries were made by the Hubble Space Telescope.

Pluto and Charon are the only members of the solar system that have as yet to receive a visit from Earth. The first space probe is expected to fly past the double planets in 2010.

Pluto and Charon

Transpluto

Both Neptune and Uranus have certain irregularities in their orbits. Astronomers assumed that this was due to the influence of another planet. This assumption became the basis for calculating the orbit of Pluto before it was ever discovered.

In the meantime, however, astronomers have come to realize that Pluto's mass, even when combined with that of Charon, does not suffice to impact the orbits of Neptune and Uranus so powerfully. Is there another celestial body beyond Pluto? In addition to the effect on orbits, the existence of comets supports this theory. The gravitational force of another outer planet could cause matter from the Oort Cloud to move towards the interior of the solar system.

The designation of this undiscovered and unproven planet is Transpluto or Planet X. Its size presumably is comparable to that of Neptune. Its orbit is assumed to be highly elliptical and perpendicular to the orbital planes of the other planets. The existence of this planet would be demonstrated if a space probe were forced to leave its calculated orbit as a result of unknown gravitational forces.

Earth

Among all the planets discovered to date, Earth is the only one to our knowledge that sustains life. When the solar system was born 4.6 thousand million years ago, Earth also was born, presumably formed out of colliding chunks of rocks.

Earth

Surface of Moon

There are two theories about the origins of Earth. According to the homogeneous theory, the rocky particles gradually bunched together and formed layers, with the lightest layer on the outside. According to the heterogeneous theory, a core of heavy matter formed first, later gathering lighter matter around it. Once the crust had cooled off, the first continents emerged. However, these broke apart again and merged anew. As a result of these repeated processes, lighter and heavier matter separated, helping to create more layers, such as one finds today in the course of geological studies of Earth's crust. The Earth consists of 70 percent water. No other planet has liquid water. Oceans and seas with their continental shelves, deep sea bottoms and trenches, oceanic ridges and many currents present an interesting and varied image. 30 percent of the surface of Earth is land, with a variety of landscapes reflecting the influences of the interior dynamics of the planet, such as volcanoes, continental drift and earthquakes, as well as radioactive processes and convection currents.

Outer influences such as the Sun, wind, rainfall, and associated erosion and weathering also determine the appearance of Earth's surface. Rivers and lakes as well as mountains and valleys provide for a great deal of variation. Depending on the climate, one might find rich vegetative growth or extensive desert regions.

Location and Structure

Earth is the third planet from the Sun. Situated between Venus and Mars, it orbits the Sun, while accompanied by its satellite, the Moon.

Earth is one of the rocky planets in the solar system. There are three principal layers: crust, mantle and core. We know relatively little about Earth's core. Presumably, temperatures in the solid inner core, which consists of nickel and iron, reach 4,000 EC. Given these tempera-

Earth

tures, one would think that the metals would stay liquid, but due to the enormous pressure they remain firm. The diameter of the inner core is estimated to be 2,400 kilometres. This is enclosed in an outer core that has a diameter of 2,000 kilometres and slightly lower temperatures. It is the only liquid layer in the interior of our planet and consists of iron and nickel. The movement in the hot rocky layer produces the magnetic field of the Earth.

The border between the outer core and the mantle is referred to as the Gutenberg discontinuity. The adjoining mantle is approximately 2,800 kilometres thick and represents the main portion of Earth's mass. It consists mostly of hot, firm silicate. The adjoining well-defined border between the mantle and the crust is called the Mohorovicic discontinuity (or Moho transition for short). It was named after Andrija Mohorovicic. In 1909, during an analysis of earthquake waves, he concluded that there had to be an abrupt change of material in this area in the interior of the planet.

In comparison to the radius of Earth, the crust is relatively thin. Beneath the oceans, the thickness of the crust ranges from 5 to 11 kilometres; below the continents it is up to 100 kilometres thick. The continental crust is very diverse. It contains stones as old as 3.8 million years. Weathering processes, together with distortion, elevations and depressions, have contributed to the development of a varied structure. The surface generally consists of sediments and volcanic rock. Beneath are piled-up metamorphosed sediment layers such as granite and crystalline stratified rock, the result of chemical reactions which constantly facilitate the development of new minerals.

The structure of the oceanic crust is relatively simple. Hardening sediments, mixed with organic particles, cover the ocean floor. This layer can be up to 3 kilometres thick. Beneath is a hard rocky layer, up to 1.5 kilometres thick. The third layer has not yet been explored sufficiently, as deep drilling has not been possible. Huge magma cones, linked to the Earth's core, stick out into this third layer. This is where new crust material is created, whenever hot magma is expelled.

The surface of the Earth consists of several so-called tectonic plates. These plates are formed by the Earth's crust in conjunction with the outermost 100 kilometres of the mantle and are referred to as the lithosphere (Greek: "stony zone"). They move along above the asthenosphere (Greek: "flowing zone"), a hotter and softer layer within the mantle.

When two tectonic plates collide, matter is folded upward, forming mountains or oceanic ridges; magma is expelled through these mountains and ridges, forming the Earth's crust.

Thus, Earth is involved in an ongoing process of change. New crust is being formed along many areas, in so-called subduction zones; at the same time, oceanic crust sinks back down into the mantle, where it melts in the deep recesses of the interior, only to rejoin the cycle. Of course, these processes can continue over many millions of years.

Meanwhile, there are also profound changes affecting life on Earth for which humans can be held responsible. Among such critical issues to be reflected upon are global warming (the greenhouse effect), the hole in the ozone layer, and acid rain.

Rotation

The Earth orbits the Sun, and it rotates about its own axis. It completes one solar orbit in 365.25 days (= 1 year). Its rotational period is one day (23 hours and 56 minutes). On the side facing the Sun it is day. On the side facing away from the Sun it is night. The angle of orbital inclination is 23.4 degrees. Hence, Earth's axis is not perpendicular to the orbital plane, resulting in seasons. Depending on the position of the axis, the North Pole and the South Pole take turns facing the Sun for approximately half a year each. The climate near the equator is far more temperate than in other regions, due to the fact that the angle of the Sun's radiation is constant.

Earth's globe is not completely round; instead, it is slightly flattened along the poles and bulges outward along the equator. During rotation, movement along the equator is faster than at the poles. The increased centrifugal force results in a slight bulging at the equator. At this point the diameter of Earth is approximately 43 kilometres longer than the polar diameter.

Earth   Sun

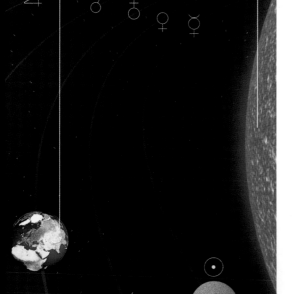

The Earth is the third planet from the Sun. It orbits the Sun in 365.25 days. Its rotational period is 23 hours and 56 minutes. It has one satellite, the Moon. The Moon's rotational period and orbital period are the same: 27.8 days.

149,600,000 km

Structure of the atmosphere

Exosphere
(height 450 – approx. 10,000 km)

Thermosphere
(height 80–450 km)

Mesosphere
(height 50–80 km)

Stratosphere
(height 10–50 km)

Troposphere
(height 0–10 km)

Ozone layer
(protects against Sun's UV rays)

Structure of Earth

Atmosphere
(nitrogen, oxygen)

Crust (silicate rock)

Mantle (silicate rock)

Outer core
(liquid iron and nickel)

Solid inner core
(iron and nickel)

Ocean

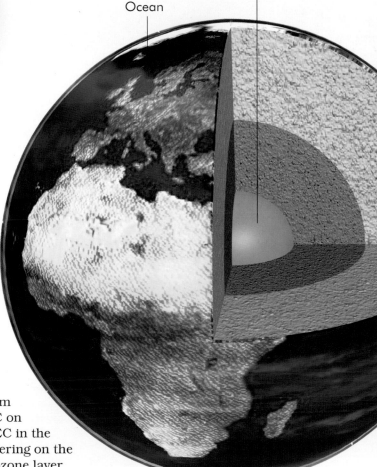

Atmosphere

The atmosphere surrounds our planet like a giant shield; without it, life on Earth would be impossible. The atmosphere consists of 78 percent nitrogen and 21 percent oxygen. There also are small amounts of argon (0.9 percent), carbon dioxide (0.04 percent), and traces of neon, hydrogen, helium, ozone, methane and nitrogen oxide.

The atmosphere can be divided into various layers: troposphere, stratosphere, mesosphere, thermosphere and exosphere. The troposphere is the area directly above the surface, the lowest layer of the atmosphere. Near the equator it reaches heights of up to 20 kilometres. Along the poles it is about 10 kilometres high. This sphere is the setting for various phenomena that affect our weather. These include rain, snow, cloud formation, storms and thunderstorms. In the troposphere temperatures range from an average of 15 EC on the ground to −60 EC in the upper regions bordering on the stratosphere. The ozone layer,

upper regions temperatures can rise to 2,000 EC.

The uppermost layer is the so-called exosphere. It extends to a height of approximately 10,000 kilo-metres. There are hardly any oxygen molecules in this layer. It represents the transition into empty space, the realm of planets, satellites and stars.

Magnetic Field

Like the other planets, Earth has a magnetic field. This magnetic field is also described as a force field that produces electric currents or fields.

Over the past 2000 years this electric field has weakened progressively. In the not too distant future it will disappear completely for a brief span of time. This is a process that has repeated itself many times over. The magnetic field reverses itself. The following helps to explain the origins of this process. When the Earth was still a gaseous sphere thousands of millions of years ago, its electric conductive matter was trapped by the magnetic force of the Sun. Electrons were set in motion. This produced electrical currents which gradually turned into a magnetic field on Earth. This magnetosphere expands far into space, but is distorted by the solar wind. The actually globular shape is squeezed together on the side closer to the Sun and lengthened on the side further away. The magnetic field is a shield against the solar wind and is indispensable for survival. One might think of this as a rod-shaped magnet located in the centre of the Earth. It is tilted 11 degrees towards the rotational axis. It is called a dipole field because of its opposing poles.

The magnetic north and south poles do not coincide with the respective geographic poles. Consequently, a compass needle shows only the approximate north/south direction.

which helps to protect the Earth against dangerous ultraviolet radiation from the Sun, is located in the stratosphere.

It filters the rays and transforms them into heat. The stratosphere reaches a height of up 50 kilometres. Temperatures range from –60 EC in the lower regions to the freezing point in the upper regions. The next layer is the mesosphere; its upper border is approximately 80 kilometres above the Earth. In its upper regions temperatures drop down to –80 EC, while the lower regions are slightly warmer, absorbing some of the heat from the stratosphere below. Meteors from outer space travel as far as the mesosphere, where they die down. The thermosphere extends to a height of 450 kilometres; temperatures in this sphere rise noticeably. It is the hottest atmospheric layer. The relatively limited number of gas molecules absorb the radiation from the Sun. In the

Magnetic field of Earth

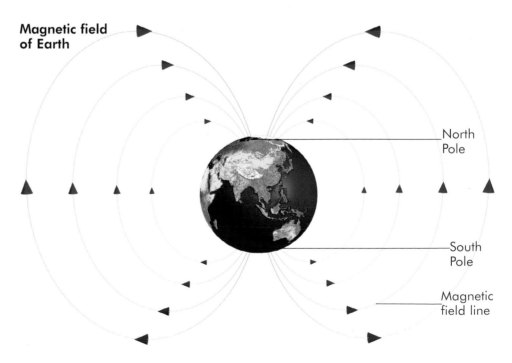

North Pole

South Pole

Magnetic field line

Earth's magnetic field expands into space. The reference points of its field lines are the North and South Poles. The magnetic force is created by the convection currents in the interior of Earth.

Earth's Moon

Our constant companion in space is the Moon. Its distance from Earth fluctuates between 356,410 and 406,740 kilometres. Its equatorial diameter is 3,476 kilometres. This is slightly more than a quarter of Earth's diameter. The Moon rotates once about its axis in 27.8 days. It needs exactly the same amount of time to complete an orbit around the Earth, meaning that it always turns the same side towards our planet.

Since the Moon does not radiate its own light, one can only see that portion illuminated by the Sun. From the Earth, this becomes apparent in the form of individual phases of the Moon from new moon to full moon, reflecting the respective positions

Theory about the birth of the Moon

Impact of celestial body on the Earth

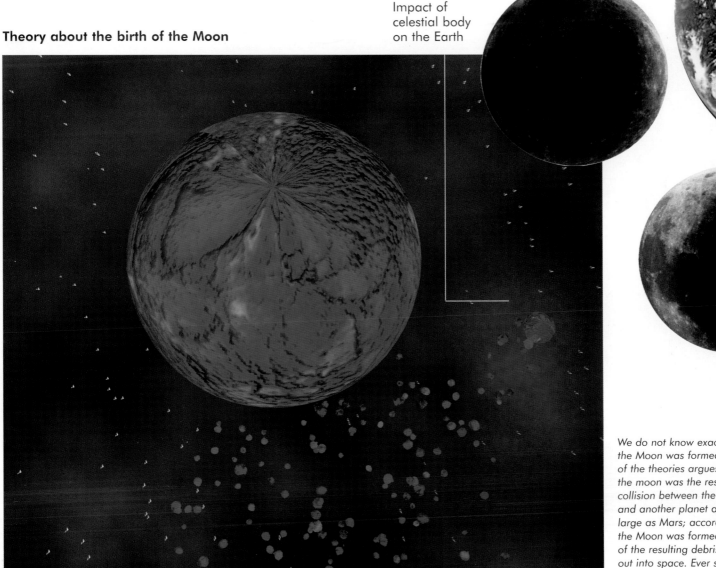

Earth

We do not know exactly how the Moon was formed. One of the theories argues that the moon was the result of a collision between the Earth and another planet about as large as Mars; accordingly, the Moon was formed out of the resulting debris flung out into space. Ever since it cooled off, the Moon has been orbiting the Earth.

Phases of the Moon

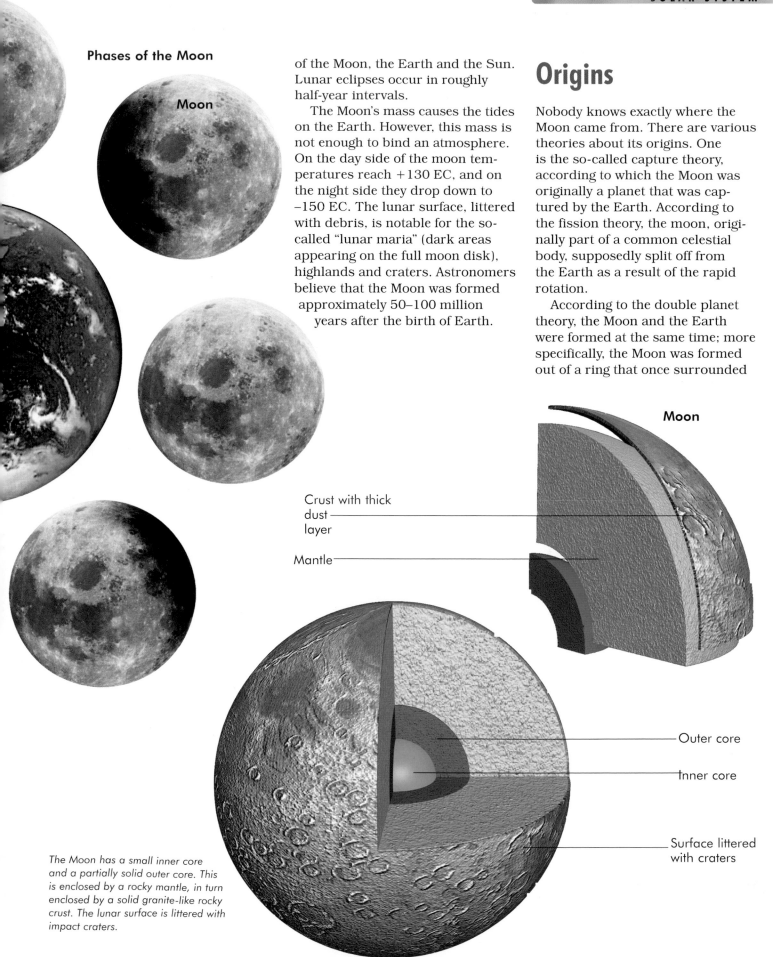

Moon

of the Moon, the Earth and the Sun. Lunar eclipses occur in roughly half-year intervals.

The Moon's mass causes the tides on the Earth. However, this mass is not enough to bind an atmosphere. On the day side of the moon temperatures reach +130 EC, and on the night side they drop down to −150 EC. The lunar surface, littered with debris, is notable for the so-called "lunar maria" (dark areas appearing on the full moon disk), highlands and craters. Astronomers believe that the Moon was formed approximately 50–100 million years after the birth of Earth.

Origins

Nobody knows exactly where the Moon came from. There are various theories about its origins. One is the so-called capture theory, according to which the Moon was originally a planet that was captured by the Earth. According to the fission theory, the moon, originally part of a common celestial body, supposedly split off from the Earth as a result of the rapid rotation.

According to the double planet theory, the Moon and the Earth were formed at the same time; more specifically, the Moon was formed out of a ring that once surrounded

Moon

Crust with thick dust layer

Mantle

Outer core

Inner core

Surface littered with craters

The Moon has a small inner core and a partially solid outer core. This is enclosed by a rocky mantle, in turn enclosed by a solid granite-like rocky crust. The lunar surface is littered with impact craters.

the Earth. This theory appears to be very plausible, because the chemical composition of the Earth's crust and that of the Moon are very similar.

Scientists studying the birth of the solar system assume that a body as large as Mars collided with the Earth during the final phase of its birth, while so-called planetesimals (hard raw materials created by condensation from the original nebula during the birth of the solar system) were captured.

During the collision, a portion of the released energy was transformed into heat, in turn causing a portion of Earth's mantle to evaporate. This portion, however, did not dissolve completely; instead, after cooling off, it condensed into a dust ring. The capture of more solid particles could have formed the Moon out of this dust ring.

Rocky wall   Meteorite   Crater (from meteorite impact)

Crater formation on the Moon

When a meteorite hits the Moon's surface, the strong impact forms a dish-shaped crater. In the process, rock is crushed and flung upward by the impact. This ends up forming a rocky wall around the crater. Large pieces of rubble that are flung into the air land again with such force that they create numerous smaller craters around the impact point.

Lunar surface

Formation of gas bubbles

Magma rising up

A volcanic crater is created when hot magma, coming from the interior, breaks through the upper layers. Gas bubbles rise through the resulting gaps. As the magma cools off, a hollow space forms under the surface. This eventually collapses, forming a crater.

Volcanic crater formation

Orbit/Movement

The Moon travels along its elliptical orbit around the Earth at a speed of 3,600 kilometres per hour. It does so in a process described as bound rotation; the rotation about its own axis takes as long as the orbit around the Earth, 27 days, 7 hours, and 43 minutes. Its distance from the Earth fluctuates between 406,740 kilometres (apogee) and 356,410 kilometres (perigee). The average distance from the Earth is 384,400 kilometres. The Moon's orbital inclination towards the ecliptic is 6.7 degrees. (The ecliptic refers to the orbit along the celestial sphere, as perceived from Earth, on which the Sun appears to be moving over the course of one year.) Given the bound rotation, the Moon always turns the same side towards the Earth. Due to an apparent wobble of the Moon, observers on Earth can see approximately 59 percent of the lunar surface. We can see this in the various phases of the moon that are the result of different degrees of illumination by the Sun.

Surface

The lunar surface is covered by a layer of debris called regolith (Greek: "coloured stone"). It consists of rocks containing calcium and aluminium particles, some of which were formed from molten lava. Scientists began to understand this after the Apollo missions in the 1960s and 70s had collected approximately 400 kilograms of moon rocks and brought this material back to the Earth for analysis. Essentially, the Moon with its up to 15-centimetre thick dust layer has an arid and desolate appearance. There is no water and no atmosphere. Given the lack of an atmosphere, there is practically no erosion at all. The thickness of the lunar crust fluctuates between 60 kilometres on the side facing the Earth and 100 kilometres on the far side. On the surface there are several dark, nearly level regions that were probably filled with molten rock during the development phase. These regions are called "maria". These dark areas are the basis of the image referred to as "The Man in the Moon". Many of these maria have romantic names such as "Bay of Rainbows" (Sinus Iridum), Sea of Honey (Mare Nectaris) and Ocean of Tranquillity (Mare Tranquillitatis). One of the largest "seas" is the Mare

Lunar phases

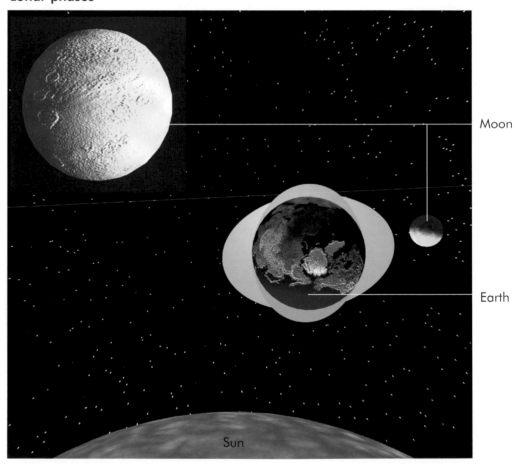

Moon

Earth

Sun

Imbrium or Sea of Rain. In that area there probably once was a crater with a diameter of approximately 1,000 kilometres, formed 4 thousand million years ago. It was filled up with molten rock from the interior of the Moon. The Mare Orientalis (Eastern Sea) on the far side of the Moon is particularly impressive. The impact of a meteorite here resulted in the formation of concentrically shaped mountain ranges.

Giant craters appearing everywhere on the moon are often surrounded by ring-shaped mountain ranges. Craters with a ray-like

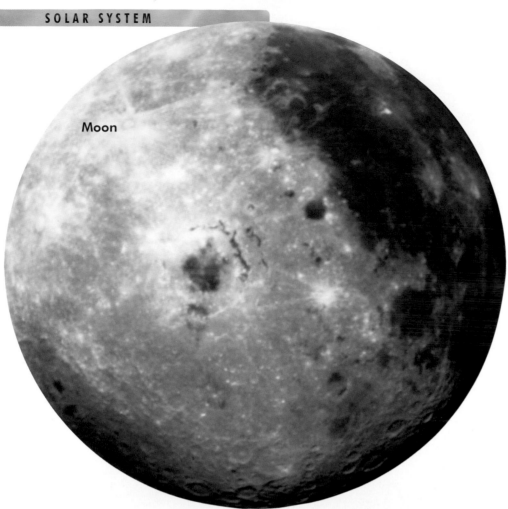

Moon

on the side facing the Earth were selected to honour famous individuals. Some of these names are Ptolemaeus, Encke and Humboldt. The craters on the far side have often been named after philosophers and scientists from the former Soviet Union.

In addition to these craters and "maria", there are many highlands with noticeable reliefs. These are called "terrae" (Latin: country, singular: terra). Many of these are the walls of giant old craters with mountains over several thousand metres in height. These terrae cover most of the surface of the Moon. Other features of the landscape include ridges, rifts, dislocations and valleys.

fringe on the edges are the result of more recent impacts. One of the most remarkable craters is the Copernicus Crater. It is estimated to be about 800 million years old. The ray-like fringes are light-coloured rocky fragments that were flung outward at impact. On the side of the Moon facing away from the Earth there are more and larger-sized craters, but fewer "maria" than on the side facing towards the Earth. The reasons for this are still unknown. The names of the craters

Lunar Effects on Earth

Despite a mean distance of 384,000 kilometres, our satellite, the Moon, affects life on Earth. Anyone who has had the experience of waiting for the tide during a holiday at the North Sea is aware of this. Water on the side of the Earth facing the Moon is attracted by the Moon and repelled on the opposing side. This causes the tides. On the open sea this results in a difference of less than one metre. However, in shallow seas the result of fluctuations can be as much as 6 metres. At river deltas the difference between high tide and low tide is even greater. The position of the Moon is the determining factor. During the waning and waxing phases, the Sun, the Moon and the Earth form a right angle, and the effect on the tides is relatively minor. When the three celestial bodies are aligned, the impact is much greater. Neap tide is the term associated with the first scenario. In the latter scenario the gravitational forces are much

Moon —————

greater, resulting in so-called spring tides.

The Sun's impact on the tides is half as great as that of the Moon. For an apparent orbit around the Earth, the Moon needs 24 hours and 50 minutes. In this time period, high tide and low tide alternate two times. Consequently, the tides shift every day by 50 minutes. It is a fact that during a full moon, many people sleep poorly and may even engage in sleepwalking. There also are statistical studies demonstrating the fact that at these times both the crime rate and the birth rate go up.

A lunar eclipse can occur only when the full moon travels across the orbit of the Earth. At that time, the Moon enters into the shadow of the Earth. The Moon does not become completely invisible, but instead appears to be dark reddish brown. This is due to the fact that a portion of sunlight at the edge of the Earth is diverted by the atmosphere into the shadow of the Earth.

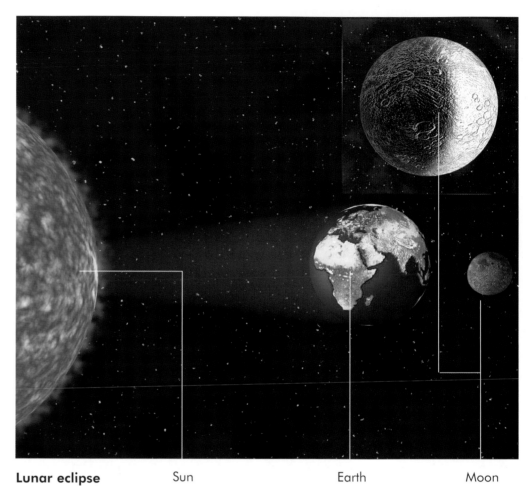

Lunar eclipse   Sun   Earth   Moon

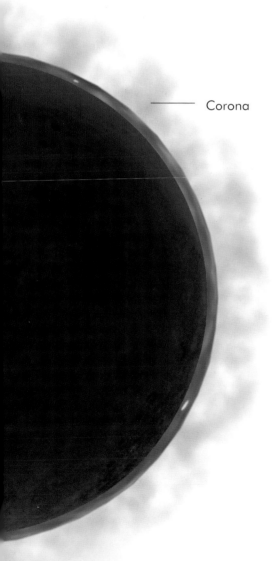

Corona

Total solar eclipse

Lunar Eclipse

A lunar eclipse occurs during a full moon. At that time, our satellite is in opposition to the Sun. The Earth is located between the Sun and the Moon. The Sun shines on the Earth, while the Earth throws a shadow. When the Moon travels through this shadow, there is a lunar eclipse. The Moon has an orbital inclination towards the Earth of approximately 56 degrees. Therefore, our satellite generally passes above or beneath the shadow cone. Otherwise, if the orbital plane were the same, every full moon would also be a lunar eclipse. The light that normally would reach the Moon directly is broken by Earth's atmosphere and then transmitted to the Moon. This process makes a lunar eclipse observable. The term partial eclipse refers to a partial passage of the satellite through the shadow cone.

47

Small Planetary Bodies

The planets with their moons and associated interplanetary matter are only some of the bodies that can be observed in space. There are many others that can be observed only rarely or with great difficulty. Given their small size, planetoids and meteors reveal themselves to us only when we use a telescope. Planetoid means "small planet". Another term used almost interchangeably is "asteroid".

If one does not associate a specific minimum size with planets, then the solar system contains not only nine planets, but rather millions of them. However, the rocky fragments located mostly inside a belt between the orbits of Mars and Jupiter add up to only a low total mass. According to estimates and calculations, this mass is no more than one tenth that of the Earth.

Meteors are remnants of comets, or even just remnants of comet tails that burn up when entering the Earth's atmosphere. When we observe them at that point in time, we think of them as shooting stars. Meteorites, finally, are those planetary bodies that are too large to burn up. When they reach the Earth, their impact produces the typical meteorite craters.

Comets

Since time immemorial, human beings have been both fascinated and frightened by comets. Often, they perceived comets as harbingers of disaster or even the end of the world. Astronomy has largely invalidated these spectres.

The European space probe Giotto played an important part in this process. In 1986, when Halley's Comet made its most recent appearance, the space probe flew past the core of the comet at a distance of approximately 500–600 kilometres.

Hale-Bopp

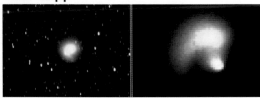

Comets originate in the outer reaches of our solar system. Their orbits are often extremely eccentric. Some comets come very close to the Sun at regular intervals. One of these is Hale-Bopp.

Since that point in time, much more information has become available about the structure and composition of comets. Nevertheless, they continue to be subject to a certain amount of mystification.

For instance, a comet was discovered in 1995 that could be observed without any optical instruments in the spring of 1997. Named Hale-Bopp after its discoverers, this comet inspired an entire sect in the United States to commit suicide. The members of this sect believed that an extraterrestrial spaceship was travelling in the wake of the comet. They also believed that they needed to divest themselves of their earthly body in order to be able to join this spaceship. The word "comet" comes from Latin, and its literal meaning is "long-haired".

Comets consist of dust and frozen gases. When a comet approaches the Sun, its surface begins to evaporate in the intense heat. This results in the formation of a huge glowing gas bubble that surrounds the core of the comet. At the same time, the solar wind creates a straight plasma tail and a slightly curved dust tail, streaming away from the Sun.

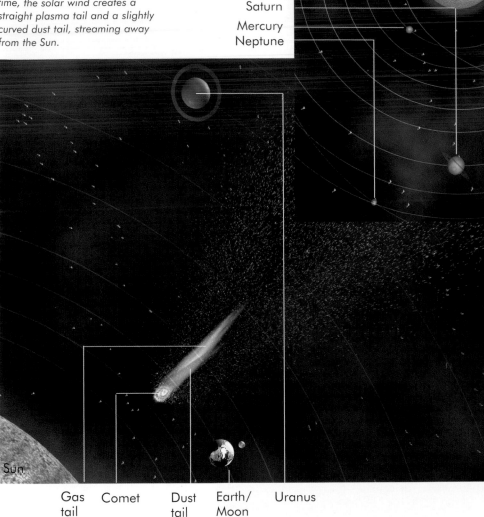

Uranus
Mars
Comet
Jupiter
Venus
Earth
Sun
Saturn
Mercury
Neptune

Sun

Gas tail   Comet   Dust tail   Earth/ Moon   Uranus

Orbits and Origins

The outer edge of our solar system consists of a cloud that is outside of Pluto's orbit. This cloud contains thousands of millions of comet cores, also called "dirty snowballs". In 1950, the Dutch astronomer Jan Oort was the first to come up with a theoretical description of this cloud. It is possible that the Oort Cloud represents the remnants of our solar system's basic building blocks. For this reason, further exploration of comets is of particularly great interest. Comets may well provide answers about the birth of planets known to date. The Oort Cloud is subject to the Sun's gravitational field. Sometimes, a core breaks off from the cloud and ends up in the orbit of one of the inner planets.

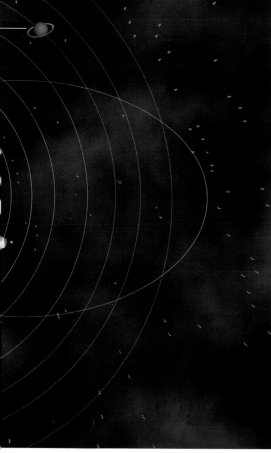

Compared to planetary orbits, the orbits of comets tend to be very eccentric. Influenced by the solar wind, a comet tail always points away from the Sun. It shrinks in size with growing distance from the Sun.

This might be the result of collisions with, or the gravitational force of, other celestial bodies. When a comet, travelling toward the Sun, passes a larger planet on the way, its orbit may be diverted. The comet ends up in a relatively narrow elliptical orbit. This turns the comet into a short-period comet – a comet that needs a relatively small number of years for one orbit around the Sun. Halley's Comet serves as a

Shoemaker-Levy Comet

A Hubble-Space-Telescope camera was used to take this picture in May 1994, when Jupiter was at a distance of 670 million kilometres from the Earth. The dark spot is the shadow of its moon Io. A short time later, the comet Shoemaker-Levy came close to the planet, and the comet was essentially ripped to shreds. One can still see a trail of icy fragments beneath Jupiter, dispersed across an expanse of 1.1 million kilometres.

case in point. It travels across Earth's orbit in 76-year intervals. It is famous above all for the fact that it is the first comet with a predicted date of return.

The British astronomer Edmund Halley had calculated the comet's orbit and announced that it would return in 1758. The comet has been reappearing again and again since at least 240 BC. During a single orbit, Halley's Comet loses approximately 200 million tons of its total weight. However, given that the comet has a relatively large mass, it will continue to traverse our Earth's orbit for another 10,000 years.

There also are comets that are not as regular. Actually, most comets are of this type. After passing by the Sun, they return to the Oort Cloud. Comets that need more than 200 years for an orbit are called long-period comets. Enck's Comet has the shortest orbit – three years and four months.

In July 1994, Jupiter knocked the comet Shoemaker-Levy-9 out of its orbit. This brought the comet into the planet's gravitational field. It broke up into several pieces, which crashed down onto Jupiter. The tremendous collisions that resulted would have sufficed to extinguish life on Earth. The discoverer of the comet, the American geologist and astronomer Eugene Shoemaker, was asked whether this could also happen to Earth. He answered: "It is not a question of whether this will happen. It would be interesting to know when it will happen."

Structure and Composition

A comet consists of a core, a coma and a tail. The core's diameter is only a few kilometres. Measurements undertaken by the space probe Giotto indicated that Halley's Comet is sixteen kilometres long and eight kilometres wide.

The core itself consists mostly of ice and dust. This is the basis for the term "dirty snowball". The core is located inside the coma, the largest part of a comet. The coma's diameter ranges from 10,000 to 100,000 kilometres. The coma is

Comet structure

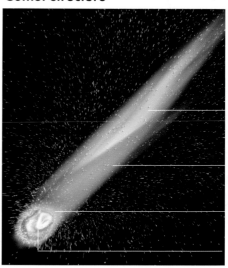

Gas tail

Dust tail

Coma (gas mantle)

Core

produced as a result of the core's approach to the Sun. Some of the ice evaporates and surrounds the core like a gas cloud. Meanwhile, the solar wind forces some of the gas away from the coma, thus creating the comet's gas tail. As soon as the comet moves away from the Sun, the gas tail then flies ahead of the comet, forced forward by the pressure of the solar wind. Solid particles detached from the core form the dust tail. This tail also points away from the Sun, albeit at a slightly curved angle.

Meteors/Meteorites

The multiplicity of similar-sounding terms such as meteor, meteorite, meteorology, meteoroid, meteor stream, or meteor shower can be confusing; it is easy to get these terms mixed up. Meteorology, the science of the atmosphere and its phenomena, especially weather, refers to all bodies that impact the Earth as meteors. This includes not only solid bodies, but other types of impact as well. In astronomy, the term meteor is used for so-called shooting stars. Small planetary bodies with a diameter of up to one metre are called meteoroids. These turn into shooting stars (or meteors) upon reaching the Earth's atmosphere. Matter from outer space that reaches the Earth's surface is called a meteorite. In mid-August every year it is possible to observe shooting star streams, also called meteor showers.

Meteorite

Origin

"In our day and age, it would be unforgivable if we lent any credibility at all to fairy tales such as the notion that iron falls from the sky." This statement was made by the mineralogist Xaver Stütz in 1792,

Meteors are light phenomena that become visible in the sky when they enter the atmosphere of the Earth. In the vernacular they are referred to as shooting stars.

despite the fact that such phenomena had already been described repeatedly in the past. One might think of, for instance, the meteorite of Ensisheim in Alsace, France that came down in 1492, or the meteorite shower of Eichstädt in Bavaria, Germany in 1785.

However, scientists came to accept the existence of meteorites only in 1803. In that year, the French Academy of Sciences received reports testifying that a rain of thousands of rocks had come down on Aigle, France. This extremely rare and profoundly impressive event – a meteorite breaking into pieces above a populated region – was finally enough to convince doubters.

Shooting stars are light phenomena that appear when cosmic dust enters the atmosphere. They are no larger than the head of a pin. Travelling at speeds of 20–70 kilometres per second, they rush towards the ground. These dust particles might be the remainders of a comet tail. There are various theories to explain how the trail of light in the sky is

created. The process of a dust particle burning up is inadequate as an explanation, since such an effect cannot be produced at a height of 80–130 kilometres.

Friction with air molecules also fails to provide a satisfactory explanation, since there are simply not enough of those available in the upper layers of the atmosphere. It is likely that the particles entering the atmosphere push air molecules along in front of them and, in the process, compress them.

There are about ten shooting stars in the sky every hour. Brighter meteors, which would presuppose a larger mass, are rarer. They are called fireballs or bolides. Larger bodies do not burn up completely. Some fragments find their way all the way down to the surface of the Earth. At that point they are called meteorites. They consist of stone or iron or a mixture of these two. The majority are stone meteorites. Interplanetary bodies do not crash to the ground as a result of the Earth's gravitational forces. Instead, the

Earth and meteorites, travelling on their respective orbits, collide. After the Murchison meteorite came down in Australia in 1969, geologists at the University of Oklahoma thought that they had enough data to substantiate their theory. Their findings were finally published in the summer of 1997. According to them, it is possible that a meteorite brought life to the Earth.

This chunk of rock from outer space allegedly contained amino acids, the basic building blocks of life. Protein molecules have a particularly large concentration of heavy nitrogen isotopes, unlike any concentration found on the Earth. Consequently, amino acids must have come from the cosmos.

Meteor Showers

Meteor showers, the visible phenomena associated with meteor streams, appear every year around the same time. The orbit of the Earth around the Sun always remains the same. On its orbit, our home planet passes large expanses of cosmic dust fields. These conglomerations of matter often come from comets' tails, the components of which also include dust. When we observe meteor showers from the Earth, it seems as if the streams originate from a single point. That apparent point of origin is called the radiant.

For instance, every year the dust tail of the comet Swift-Tuttle causes a fabulous show in the sky called the Perseids. From the end of July to the middle of August, we can observe a cluster of shooting stars. Sometimes as many as one hundred appear in the sky. The radiant of this meteor shower is located in the constellation Perseus, hence the name Perseids.

Other meteor showers are the Aquarids and Orionids, caused by Halley's Comet. They occur in May and October respectively. The Earth moves across the dust tail of Halley's Comet twice.

Meteor streams

Impacts

Even though iron meteorites are found on Earth more frequently than stone meteorites, they are rarer. Up to 95 percent of all meteorites consist of stone. This paradox is due to the fact that stone meteorites are less noticeable on the surface of the Earth. They also weather more rapidly.

The largest meteorite found to date was discovered in Namibia in 1920. The Hoba meteorite, consisting of iron, weighs approximately 60 tons. Craters with dimensions by far exceeding those of the Hoba meteorite suggest that in the past far more voluminous stone and iron fragments impacted the Earth. When weight exceeds 100 tons, the released energy is too great. Stones that weigh so much would disintegrate completely upon impact. For this reason, it has not been possible to find more than traces of interplanetary matter in such craters despite intensive search efforts. A familiar site in this context

Meteorite crater in Arizona

is the Barringer Meteor Crater at Winslow in Arizona, USA. It is almost circular, with a diameter of approximately 1.2 kilometres and a depth of about 170 metres. The meteor must have been 30 metres large, with a weight of 150,000 tons. In Nördlinger Ries in Bavaria, Germany, a catastrophe of unimaginable dimensions occurred approximately 15 million years ago. The meteorite that crashed down left a crater behind that has a diameter of 23 kilometres. The released energy was a thousand times that of the bomb in Hiroshima. According to some scientists, 65 million years ago an even more momentous impact caused the extinction of the dinosaurs.

Meteor   Meteors   Earth

Interplanetary Matter

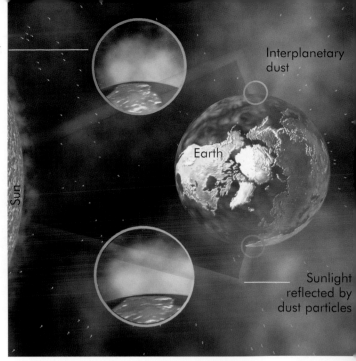

The interaction of the Sun's energy with the "smallest of the smallest" particles that make up interplanetary matter produces certain effects.

One of these effects is the zodiacal light. It can be observed especially at the equator at sunrise and sunset. The light of the corona is another such effect. It surrounds the Sun and can be observed during a complete solar eclipse. There also are gases in interplanetary space that are formed for the most part by the solar wind.

Zodiacal light (dust particles in the solar system)

On a clear night, you can occasionally see the zodiacal light. It is caused by the reflection of sunlight by small interplanetary dust particles, in particular in the space between the Sun and the orbit of the Earth. The zodiacal light can be seen as a pale ribbon of light that stands out against the customary twilight.

Zodiacal Light

Just before sunrise and directly after sunset, you can observe an increasing brightness in the sky in the area where the Sun seems to appear all of a sudden every morning and where it disappears in the evening.

You can see this light particularly well at the equator. In our latitudes, you would be able to observe it only rarely. You can see it only in the spring right after sunset and in the fall before sunrise.

Clear visibility unaffected by other sources of light is required for this. The zodiacal light should not be confused with the twilight during an actual sunrise or sunset. It does not cover the entire sky, but rather appears cone-shaped and even triangular all along the ecliptic.

The ecliptic is the apparent orbit of the Sun over the course of one year. In the course of this orbital progression, the Sun passes the various signs of the zodiac. This is the origin of the term zodiacal light (from the Greek word zodiacus = circle of animals). This apparition is produced by a dust cloud that orbits the Sun, dispersing its light. The interplanetary dust was created by the collision of larger planetary bodies (meteorites, comets, etc.).

Solar wind

Solar wind particles

Coronal Light

The corona is the layer that envelops the Sun. This outer atmosphere of the Sun cannot normally be seen with the unaided eye. The surface of the Sun, known as the photosphere, prevents this with its enormous brightness. We can see the corona only during a complete solar eclipse. Incidentally, the name corona derives from the word "crown".

The corona is created by the reflection of the sunlight off free electrons and also by the reflection of light off the interplanetary dust.

The corona reaches far into our solar system with its ribbon-shaped tentacles. The coronal light merges into the zodiacal light.

Coronal light

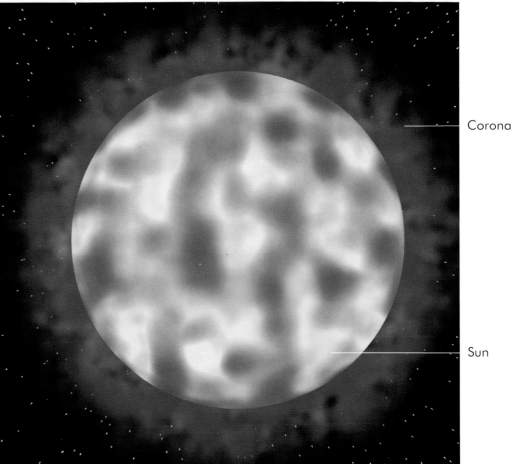

Corona

Sun

The Sun's coronal light is the result of the reflection of sunlight by interplanetary dust and free electrons.

Earth   Magnetic sphere

Solar Wind/Gases

Interplanetary gases are created mostly by the solar wind. Only a relatively small portion originates in the atmosphere of the planets. These gases consist predominantly of electrons, protons and helium cores. Depending on the force of the solar activity, these particles can reach speeds of up to 300 to 800 kilometres per second.

The Earth's magnetic field stops the streaming solar wind particles and traps them in the Van-Allen belt. A stronger solar wind could dislodge the particles again from this inner radiation belt of the magnetic field. In that process, they slip into the atmosphere, causing the polar aurora (northern lights). Within the Earth's atmosphere, the density of the solar wind particles is still five to ten atoms per cubic centimetre.

Solar wind is the term used for the electrically charged particles streaming away from the Sun as a result of radiation pressure. These particles give the magnetic field that surrounds the Earth a teardrop shape. When solar wind particles are trapped by the geographic poles, they create the polar aurora (northern lights).

Planetoids

Planetoids are located on a belt between the planets Mars and Jupiter. The first planetoid was discovered in 1801. Initially, astronomers believed it to be another planet in our solar system, naming it Ceres.

Another term used almost interchangeably with planetoid is asteroid. Planetoid means "small planet", while asteroid means "small star".

By now, we have been able to record more than 5,000 of these small planets. However, it is generally accepted that in the future many more will be discovered in the asteroid belt. Despite the large number of planetoids, their total mass is less than 10 percent of that of the Earth.

Planetoids

relative size compared to the Moon)

Moon

Ceres

Pallas

Vesta

Juno

Discovery

In our solar system, there is a remarkably large gap between Mars, the last of the inner planets, and Jupiter, the first of the outer planets. Towards the close of the 18th century, astronomers embarked on a systematic search for the "missing planet" between Mars and Jupiter.

It was by pure chance however that the Italian astronomer Giuseppe Piazzi eventually discovered a small planet on New Year's Eve 1801. He had actually been observing the stars, when he happened upon a small celestial body that later was named Ceres.

In the following years, the astronomers Olbers and Harding discovered the planetoids Pallas, Juno and Vesta. Vesta is the brightest of these, while Ceres, with a diameter of approximately 933 kilometres, is the largest. Almost every year

since 1845, more planetoids have been discovered in the asteroid belt between Mars and Jupiter. At this time, we know of more than 5,000 such bodies. However, it is possible that more than 10,000 travel around inside this belt.

Planetoids are not all located inside the asteroid belt. The planetoids Icarus, Hidalgo and Amor, for instance, have greatly inclined orbits. In 1893, the planetoid Brucia was the first to be discovered by astrophotography, a method pioneered in 1891. Phaeton was the first to be found by a space probe in 1983.

Orbits

Most planetoids orbit the Sun while travelling along the asteroid belt (or planetoid belt) between the orbits of Mars and Jupiter. Are these the fragments of another planet once in our solar system?

The first to voice this idea in the early 19th century was Heinrich Olbers, the discoverer of the planetoids Pallas and Vesta. In 1972, the Canadian astronomer Michael

planet would have had to have 90 times the mass of the Earth.

All planetoids together do not even have the mass of our Moon. This calculation takes into account the other asteroids, whose existence is only assumed even though they have not yet been discovered. Their size clearly is less than that of the larger-mass planetoids such as Ceres. Presumably, Jupiter's gravitational force has prevented these asteroids from clumping together into a single planet. Outside the asteroid belt, there are planetoids with elliptical and sharply inclined orbits. Some of these planetoids, for instance Apollo

and Amor, cut across the orbit of the Earth. The ellipsis of the asteroid Hidalgo reaches almost as far as the orbit of Saturn. There are two groups of planetoids travelling on Jupiter's orbit, called Trojans.

One group of Trojans travels 60 degrees ahead of the planet, the other group is following 60 degrees behind. This circumstance makes it possible for the planetoids to remain on the orbit. If one of the groups did not exist, or if the spacing were irregular, the constellation would not be stable. Jupiter, with its large mass, would throw the planetoids out of orbit.

Orbits of several typical planetoids

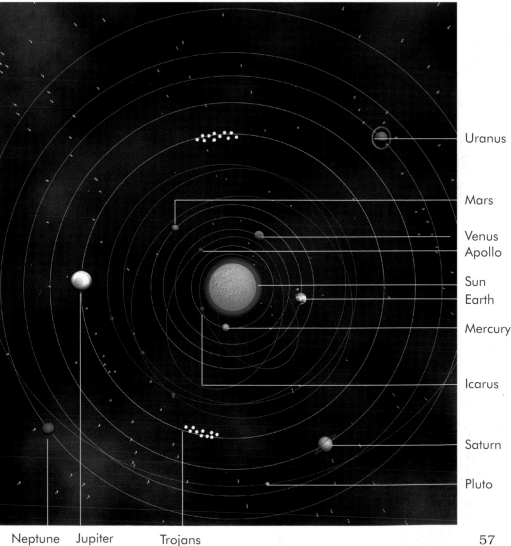

Uranus

Mars

Venus
Apollo

Sun
Earth

Mercury

Icarus

Saturn

Pluto

Neptune   Jupiter   Trojans

Ovenden "proved" this idea at the University of Vancouver. He noted that the planetary orbits do not have an ideal, stable position. According to his calculations, a planet that had been orbiting the Sun in 2.8 AU (astronomical units) was destroyed more than 15 million years ago. This would correspond with the location of today's asteroid belt, at a distance of 300–500 million kilometres from the Sun. Currently, however, this theory is considered untenable. Such a

Galaxies

100,000,000,000 – according to estimates, this is the number of galaxies in the universe (100 thousand million). Even though galaxies vary greatly in terms of size, astronomers have settled on a mean value. Accordingly, the average number of stars inside a galaxy is likewise 100 thousand million. Using telescopes, it has already been possible to explore several of these massive conglomerations of stars, gas and dust.

Galaxies – the name comes from galaxis, the Greek word for milk – are grouped according to their shapes. There are elliptical, barred, irregular (that is, without a recognizable shape) or spiral galaxies. Our Milky Way is a spiral. The mean size of spiral galaxies is 100,000 light-years across. Galaxies revolve around a common central point.

One revolution of the Milky Way takes about 230 million years. However, such conglomerations of stars are not isolated in space. They are joined in clusters. The cluster to which the Milky Way belongs is referred to as the Local Group. In this system there are approximately thirty other galaxies. The largest and most well-known of these is the Andromeda Nebula. In addition to groups and galaxy clusters, other forms of conglomeration are double or multiple systems.

Our Milky Way

The word "galaxy" comes from the Greek, made up of "gala" (milk) and "cyclos" (cycle). Greek mythology offers one of the earliest explanations of the origin of the Milky Way. When the goddess Hera was nursing Hercules, some of her milk escaped and sprayed as a milky band across the skies. According to the scientific explanation, gaseous matter created by the Big Bang compressed to form stars inside of galaxies.

Our Milky Way is a spiral-shaped galaxy. If we were to look at it from above, we would see a fire wheel. Looking at it from the side, we would see a disk with a spherical bulge in the centre.

The Milky Way extends across 100,000 light-years. Along the outer areas (spiral arms) it extends across 3,000 light-years, along the centre 15,000 light-years.

It is very difficult to observe the galaxy's core area, since even strong telescopes cannot penetrate the interstellar dark nebulae.

This complicates any exploration, but it does not mean it is impossible. In radio astronomy, measurements are absolutely possible. The core's diameter is 3,250 light-years. It contains mostly stars called red giants. Measurements have settled on a point in the middle of the core as the strongest source of radio waves; this point was named Sagittarius A. But this does not tell us whether there is a black hole in the axis of the Milky Way or whether there is a rapidly revolving large-mass giant star at that central point.

Structure

The total number of stars in the Milky Way exceeds 100 thousand million. Some astronomers even believe that this figure should be doubled.

It will never be possible for human beings to look at the Milky Way from the outside. However, given various parameters, we have concluded that it has a spiral shape.

Since we can see other spiral-shaped galaxies, we also know – at least roughly – what our Milky Way looks like. If we were to look at it from the side, we would see a plane with a flattened spherical shape in the centre. If we were to look down on the galaxy, we would see a fire wheel. This spiral has a core and presumably four main arms. The Milky Way is surrounded by a spherical halo, consisting mainly of spherical star clusters and variable stars of the type RR Lyrae. Another assumption is that the halo is surrounded by a corona that is formed out of thin hydrogen plasma.

Galaxy cluster

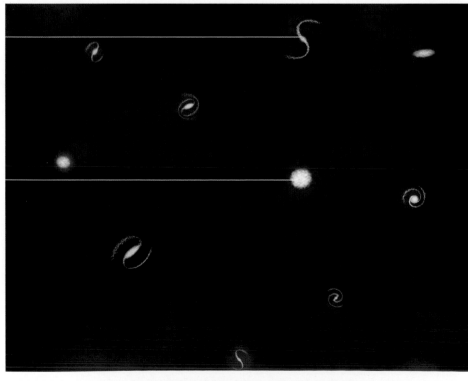

Barred spirals

Elliptical galaxies

Star systems comparable to our Milky Way are called galaxies. We distinguish between various types such as normal and barred spiral nebulae, elliptical and irregular galaxies.

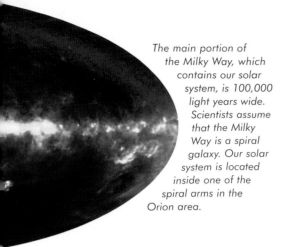

The main portion of the Milky Way, which contains our solar system, is 100,000 light years wide. Scientists assume that the Milky Way is a spiral galaxy. Our solar system is located inside one of the spiral arms in the Orion area.

Rotation

Our Milky Way is not a structure fixed in space. It revolves around a central point. The galaxy has the shape of a spiral with four arms. The spiral arms have been named Crux-Centauris, Perseus, Orion and Sagittarius.

Our solar system is located on the edge of the Orion arm. While Earth orbits the Sun, the entire solar system together with all the stars revolves around the centre of the Milky Way. The Sun and its planets rush through space at a speed of approximately 220 kilometres per second. Yet, our system needs more than 200 million years for one complete revolution. Since the birth of the solar system over 4.5 thousand million years ago, not even two dozen revolutions have been completed.

The dynamics of our galaxy's rotational velocity are not the same as those of firm bodies. Starting at the centre, it first moves upward towards the outside and then slowly descends again. Along the outer edges of the galaxy, the speed presumably increases again, possibly suggestive of the gravitational force of other galaxies.

The differences described above also depend on the individual stars' rotations. The stars and globular star clusters in the halo of our galaxy orbit the centre along elongated elliptical orbits. There are star clusters with up to 1 million individual stars far outside the plane of the spiral arms. Some of these swing outwards from the core and back again.

Population of Stars

In the first time period following the Big Bang, clouds formed out of hydrogen and helium. Gaseous spheres developed out of these clouds, compressing to the point of nuclear meltdown. In this way, 90 percent of the Milky Way's gas mass was transformed into stars. The remaining gas matter flattened off towards the sides.

Here as well, stars formed and continue to form in a slow but steady rhythm. A great concentration of stars is in the middle of our galaxy.

There and in the star clusters of the halo, there are hardly any new formations. There is no longer a sufficient amount of gas mass available for such a process.

Along the outer areas of the Milky Way, which is, after all, approximately 3,000 light-years wide, new stars form inside and between the spiral arms. In the mid-20th century Walter Baade divided the population of stars into two groups.

The younger and middle-aged stars (including our Sun) are in Population 1. They are located mostly in the main disk of the galaxy and, relatively speaking, contain many heavy elements.

Star clusters in the halo belong to Population 2. These stars are significantly older (up to 10 thousand million years) and have hardly any elements heavier than helium. The core of the Milky Way also consists mostly of Population 2 stars.

Spiral arms   Core   Dust clouds

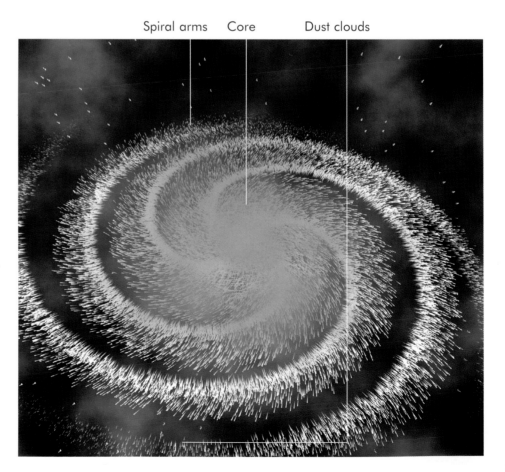

Classification

As early as the 18th century, Immanuel Kant had already claimed that the nebulae visible in the night sky were other star systems. Later, Alexander von Humboldt coined an expression still used today – "world islands". Nevertheless, during the 19th century people continued to believe that these nebulae were a part of our own Milky Way.

Kant's hypothesis was finally confirmed in the 1920s. The American astronomer Edwin Hubble observed these nebulae with a large telescope from the top of Mt. Wilson in the United States. He discovered that these nebulae are galaxies just like our Milky Way. Furthermore, these galaxies exhibited differing structures.

Hubble developed a system for classifying the galaxies according to their form. Accordingly, Hubble distinguishes between elliptical galaxies, barred spirals and normal spirals; he breaks each of these down further into subgroups: E0 to E7 for elliptical galaxies, Sa to Sm for normal spirals, and SBa to SBm for barred spirals. A transitional type between spiral-shaped and elliptical galaxies has characteristics of both; Hubble identifies this type as S0.

It is also possible to classify galaxies on the basis of categories of luminosity, ranging from I to V. Category I refers to galaxies with the greatest luminosity (super giant galaxies), while category V represents galaxies with the least luminosity (dwarf galaxies). The Milky Way falls under category III (normal giant galaxy).

Elliptical Galaxies

Elliptical galaxies are broken down into subgroups E0 to E7. This classification scheme is based on the degree of the ellipsis. E0 refers to "nearly round", while E7 refers to a flat elliptical shape. These galaxies contain hardly any gas or dust clouds, the building blocks for new suns. Therefore, elliptical galaxies contain hardly any populations of stars. There are mostly older red stars. Consequently, these galaxies actually have a more reddish appearance than spiral nebulae. The interior structures have high levels of density. Thus, it is not possible to explore these structures very well. For a long time, astronomers assumed that the various galaxy forms represented different developmental phases. Accordingly, they thought that ellipses turn into spirals. This is not the case. Spiral nebulae constantly give birth to new stars. In the categories E0 to Sc of the Hubble classification, there is a steep increase in the amount of interstellar matter, required for the formation of stars. It is considered indisputable that elliptical galaxies are older than spiral galaxies.

Hubble's Tuning Fork Diagram

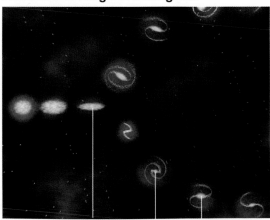

Elliptical galaxies Normal spirals Barred spirals

Low density in outer area   Globular cluster

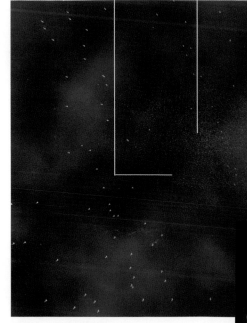

Elliptical galaxy

Spiral galaxies have a spherical arrangement of old stars in their centre. Their spiral arms contain nebulae and, more importantly, young stars.

Elliptical giant galaxy

Spiral galaxy

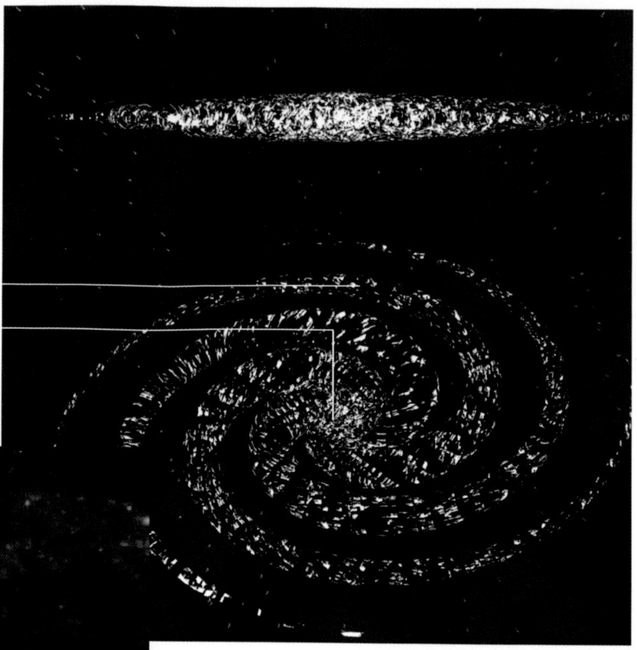

Side view →

Spiral arms

Core

Top view →

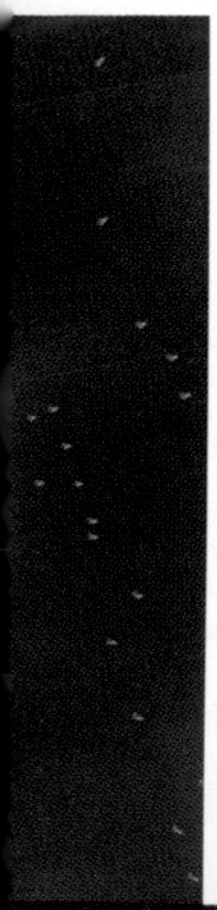

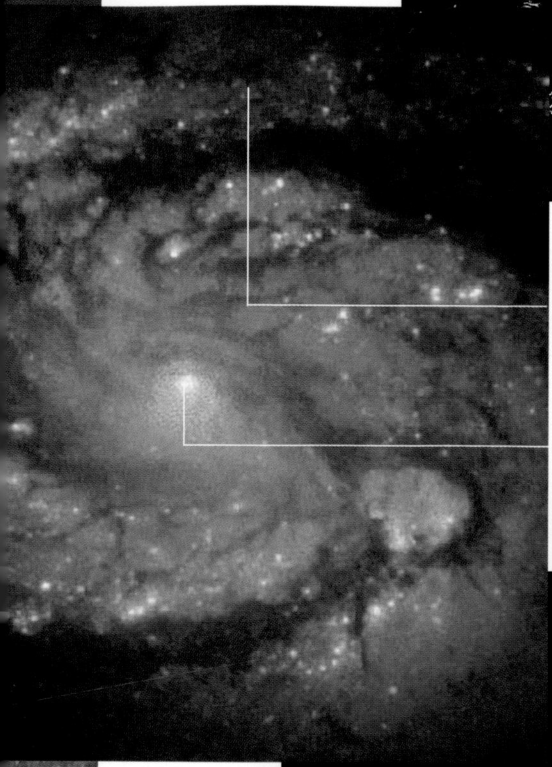

Spiral arms with dust and nebulae contain young stars.

Central area contains old stars.

Barred spirals have a straight bar, appearing widest at the centre and both fainter and thinner towards the ends. At the respective ends of the bar, spiral arms are attached at a right angle. The cores have different degrees of development, while the arms can be curved to a greater or lesser degree.

Spiral galaxy

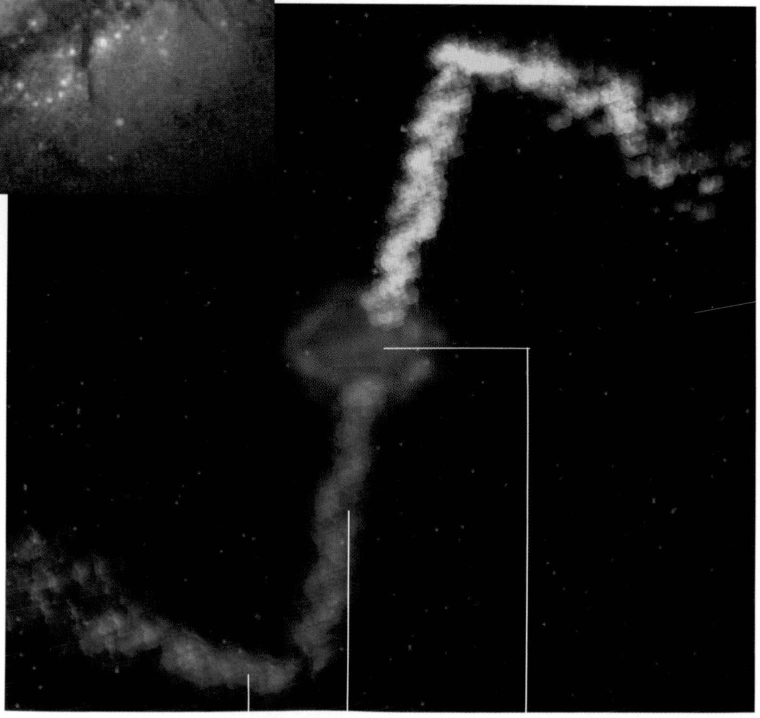

Barred spiral   Spiral arm   Bar   Core

Spiral Galaxies

In this group of galaxies we distinguish between normal spirals and barred spirals. They are grouped into subclasses according to the definition of the core. In the case of normal spirals, the categories are Sa to Sc.

Category Sa means that the centre of the galaxy is large and the arms are wound tightly. Sb refers to a medium-sized core and less tightly wound arms. Sc refers to a small or barely defined centre and loose arms or arms that are far apart.

There is a corresponding subdivision of barred spirals into SBa, SBb, and SBc. The S0 galaxy has a special position in this classification. The spiral arms are non-existent or very faint, while the core is well developed. In a spiral galaxy, stars revolve around the centre while travelling in the same direction. The spiral arms are practically dragged along.

The respective form suggests the rotational velocity. The arms presumably are created by density waves. These compression waves, causing increased density along the wave peaks, contribute to an increase in the population of stars.

An example for a spiral galaxy other than the Milky Way is our large neighbour, the Andromeda Nebula. This galaxy contains approximately 300 thousand million solar masses. Our Milky Way is a medium-sized spiral galaxy. A spiral is the most frequent shape in which galaxies appear.

Irregular galaxies

Irregular galaxies are without a recognizable structure. Generally, their size does not exceed a third of the size of elliptical or spiral galaxies. Presumably, their irregular structures are due to gravitational disruptions by large galaxies.

Irregular Galaxies

In addition to classified galaxies, there are those without any recognizable structure. They are not included in Hubble's classification scheme. These irregular galaxies are grouped into Type I and Type II. An example for Type II is the Magellan Cloud. This galaxy contains hot young stars with a high proportion of interstellar matter from which new stars could form.

Type II galaxies mostly contain stars that would fit into Baade's classification of Population 2 stars. In other words, there are more old stars with few heavy elements in these galaxies.

The dimension of irregular galaxies generally does not reach more than a third of that of the ellipses and spirals described in Hubble's classification scheme.

Galaxy Clusters

Generally, galaxies are part of larger conglomerations. These are called galaxy clusters. The number of galaxies in a cluster ranges from several dozen to several thousand.

In the case of a lower number, one uses the term galaxy group. There also are associations of several galaxy clusters, the so-called super clusters.

This classification of galaxy clusters is by no means arbitrary. Galaxy clusters are cosmological units sharing the same escape velocity and linked by gravity.

The average size of a cluster is 10–30 million light-years.

The Local Group is one of the most well-known galaxy clusters. It contains approximately 30 different galaxies, including our own and the Andromeda Nebula.

The Local Group

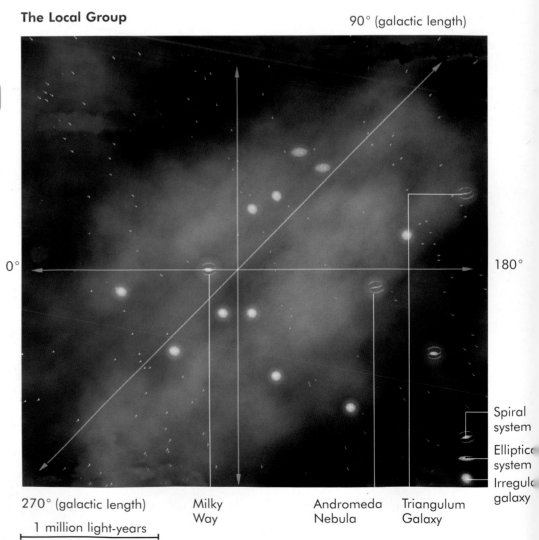

90° (galactic length)

0°

180°

270° (galactic length)

1 million light-years

Milky Way

Andromeda Nebula

Triangulum Galaxy

Spiral system

Elliptical system

Irregular galaxy

Quasar

Quasars appear to be star-like objects that are very far away from us. Presumably, these are galaxies in their beginning phases that transmit tightly bound rays from a radiating core out into space. It is possible that a large-mass black hole provides the energy for this process.

Our Milky Way is part of the so-called Local Group, which has a diameter of 6 million light-years. The largest galaxy in the Local Group is the Andromeda Nebula, at a distance of approximately 2.2 million light-years from us.

The next closest larger galaxy cluster is the Virgo cluster, 60 million light-years away. This cluster contains thousands of galaxies. The Local Group and Virgo are part of the same super cluster, which in turn has a diameter of 100 million light-years. Calculations and observations suggest that there are also super clusters with a length of more than 1 thousand million light-years.

Quasars

"Quasar" is a word created by Professor Chiu of Columbia University; it is the abbreviation of "quasi-stellar radio waves". The increasing use of radio telescopes after World War II facilitated the discovery of phenomena that would not have revealed themselves to the unaided human eye.

Two objects, 3C48 and 3C273, were discovered with the aid of radio telescopes, and it was possible to assign them to visible celestial objects. An analysis of the phenomenon known as red-shift produced astounding results. Quasars are very far away and move at a tremendous speed. The already mentioned quasar

Accretion disk   Radiative centre   Beam of rays

3C273 moves at 16 percent of the speed of light. 3C48 even moves at 36 percent; this is equivalent to approximately 108,000 kilometres per second.

In the meantime, approximately 1,500 quasars have been recorded. Some of these move at 90 percent the speed of light. Presumably, they are as far or farther than 15 thou-

sand million light-years away, thus figuring among the oldest objects in the universe. 3C273 shines with a brightness 100 billion times that of our Sun.

Perhaps these are the birthplaces of our galaxies. Looking at quasars is also a way of looking at the past, perhaps as far back as the origins of the universe.

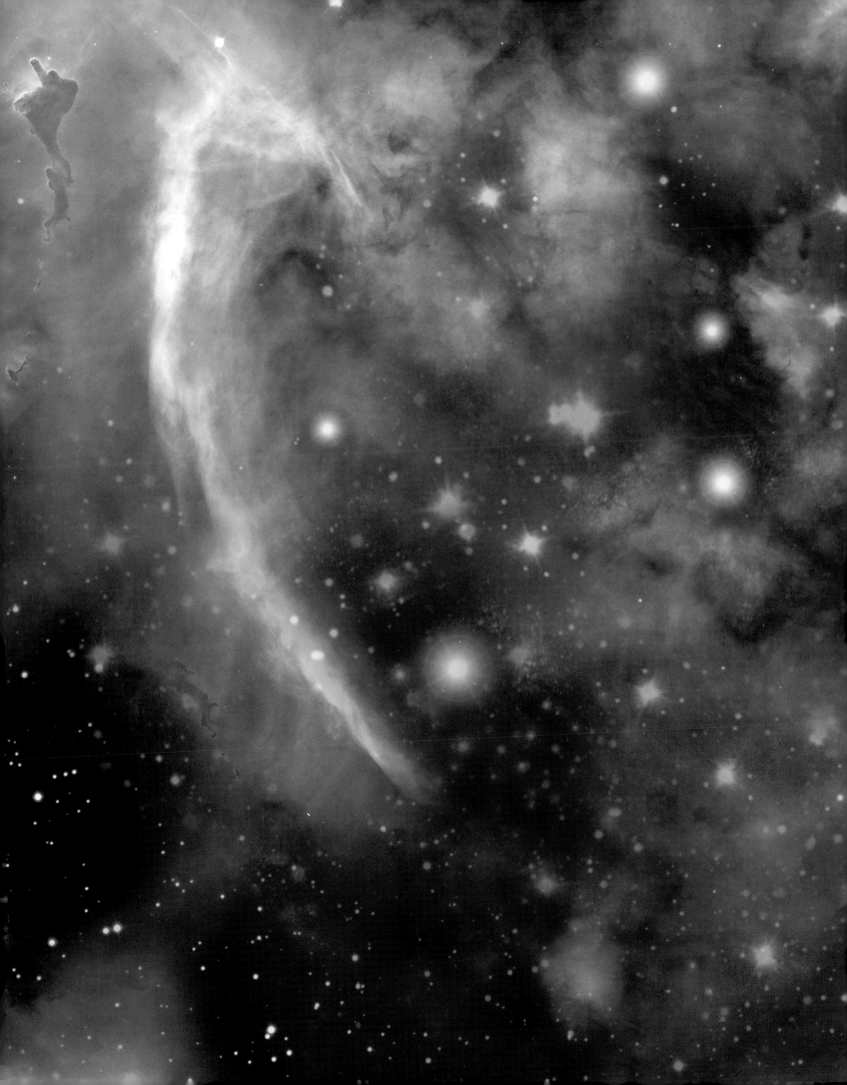

Star Systems

When we look up at the night sky, we can recognize as many as 3,000 stars. Recently, astronomers, using refractors, telescopes, and observatories, discovered that stars are not loners in the sky. They appear in various types of open to more fixed associations. Some clusters are open, others spherical. Larger conglomerations are referred to as galaxies and galaxy clusters. These connections and systems dictate the rotational direction as well as velocity of stars.

Human beings have created their own systems. Drawing on apparent similarities with myths, animals, and objects, human beings devised the constellations. Often, these are rather haphazard in their combinations. In many constellations, individual member stars are not actually a part of a single physical system. They revolve in different directions and at different speeds.

The respective distances to our solar system also vary greatly. This suggests that in the future these constellations will look completely different. However, given the enormous distances involved, this effect will be apparent only many thousands of years later. Nevertheless, the constellations definitely have their uses. For one, they help human beings to orient themselves; for another, they are of central importance to those who pursue astrology.

Stars

The term "star" is used for all bodies that appear in the sky as sources of light. Unlike planets, stars have their own source of light. Stars are created out of large gas and dust clouds as a result of the force of gravity. Depending on their respective size, mass, and composition, stars can be seen to go through different developmental phases. The protostar phase is succeeded by the stable main-sequence phase.

As soon as all energy has been consumed, the chemical composition of the star alters and it begins to "die". A star's energy comes from nuclear fusion. Light atomic cores are joined to form heavier ones. Loss of mass ensures the transformation into energy. Large amounts of heat and mass are indispensable in order to sustain nuclear fusion over longer periods of time. Depending on the respective mass of a star, the subsequent phase might be a relatively quiet death as a white dwarf or a galactic catastrophe as a nova or supernova.

Stars have different colours. Light blue stars are very hot. Their sur-face temperature is approximately 35,000 EC. As a comparison, one might consider our yellow Sun with its temperature of approximately 6,000 EC. Red stars are the coolest, with tem-peratures not exceeding 3,000 EC.

Stars are not lone rangers. Many are a part of a binary sys-tem or a multiple system. Larger groupings include star clusters, galaxies, and galaxy clusters.

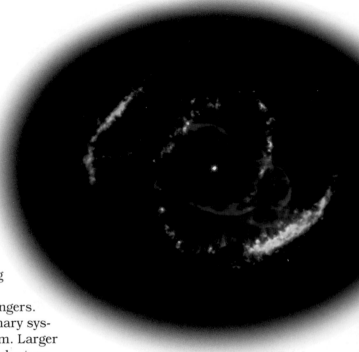

Planetary nebula

Rotation of stars

CASSIOPEIA

50,000 years ago	2005	50,000 years from now

Stars move through space at relatively high speeds. However, due to their enormous distance from the Earth, human beings can perceive any change in the stars' positions only after 50,000 to 100,000 years.

Birth/Development

The basic building blocks necessary for the formation of a star are to be found in interstellar matter. This matter consists of dust clouds and gases, appearing in varying concen-trations in space. When such clouds are drawn together as a result of gravitational forces, pressures and temperatures rise.

The steadily increasing pressure creates so much heat in the cloud core that nuclear fusion is initiated. The amount of interstellar matter is critical. The more particles there are, the more rapidly the required process of contraction can come about. A balance of forces is neces-sary for bringing about the dynamics required for the creation of a star.

Gravitational force, resulting in the process of contraction, is combined with centrifugal force. This prevents a further contraction of the cloud. During the first devel-opmental phase, the structure is still referred to as a protostar. It is surrounded by a mantle of dust. This dust falls onto the young star and as a result releases the visible light. The mantle becomes transparent as the cloud density decreases.

During nuclear fusion, hydrogen is turned into helium. Thus, mass is transformed into energy. Now the star has "matured". Radiation pressure ensures stability. The mass of the star determines the length of time it can remain in equilibrium. However, this does not mean that the more massive the star, the longer lived it will be.

Quite the contrary: massive stars consume their energy, that is, hydro-gen, much faster. A lot of matter re-sults in relatively rapid development, but at the same time in a relatively short phase of stability.

Movement

When we observe stars in the night sky, they appear to be fixed in space. For this reason they are sometimes referred to as fixed stars. However, this is only an illusion. In reality, stars move at extremely high speeds. An observer cannot really perceive this movement, because stars are so very far removed from the Earth. In order to be able to recognize changes in a constellation, one would have to look up at the sky for a good ten thousand years. Time frames that range from half a lifetime to an entire lifetime are used to determine the speed of a star's rotation. In addition to their sideways movement, stars are either approaching or travelling farther away from us. The speed of this movement is referred to as radial velocity. It is revealed by the so-called Doppler effect. The change in the spectral colours is measured. When a star comes closer, this creates a colour shift towards violet, a so-called blueshift, in other words, towards the short-wave end of the spectrum. When a star moves farther away, this results in redshift, a shift towards the long-wave end of the spectrum.

Radial velocity is rendered in positive kilometres (during removal) and negative kilometres (during approach) per second. Astronomers have determined that several of those objects farthest away in our universe, the so-called quasars, travel at nearly the speed of light.

Energy

Depending on mass and age, stars have different energy values. For a correlation of temperature and brightness, astronomers use the Hertzsprung-Russel Diagram.

E. Hertzsprung and H.N. Russel developed this system at the beginning of the 20th century.

The diagonal or main sequence shows those stars that are in their stable phase (main-sequence stars). Our Sun is in this phase. In this phase, incidentally the largest portion of a star's life cycle, hydrogen is turned into helium.

Every star has a supply of fuel that provides for an even radiation of energy. The Sun's reserve will last for another 5 thousand million years. Accordingly, it has already consumed about half of its available energy. The Sun is an average star with a medium surface temperature and accordingly medium luminosity.

A star with less heat albeit the same size radiates less energy.

The diagram shows that stars do not remain the same; instead, they eventually leave the main-sequence phase. Once the Sun's energy reserves are used up, it will change.

When massive stars approach the end of their lives, their luminosity increases once more. The star expands and turns red. This is an effect of the cooling-off period, when no more additional energy can be produced. Finally, the red giant collapses, once the force of gravity exceeds the radiation pressure.

Gravitational force compresses the star. The pressure results in a great deal of heat. The limited size (it shrinks down to the size of a planet) results in reduced luminosity.

Hertzsprung-Russel Diagram

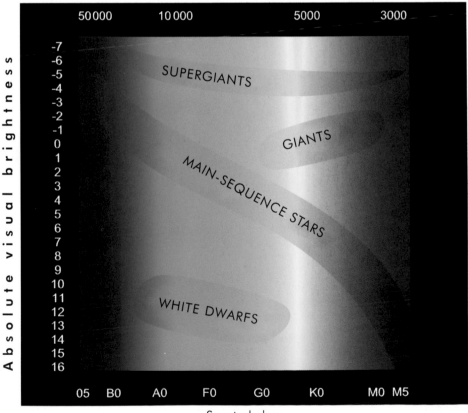

Star Types

For us, gazing up at the vast sky, stars look alike. Yet, there are many different types, different sizes, and different developmental phases. For example, there are red giants, white dwarfs and neutron stars. Binary stars that orbit a common centre of gravity are very interesting. So-called variable stars represent a special class of stars. Their radiation, as well as occasionally their size, change in intervals of minutes, hours, or days. They are not among those stars with a normal development spaced out over thousands of years.

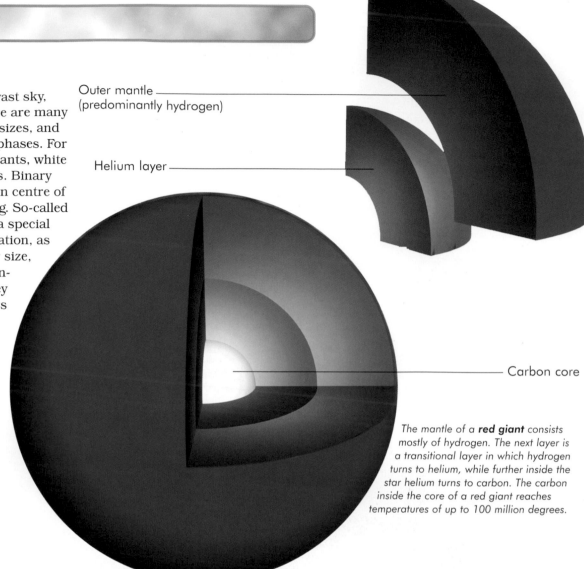

Outer mantle (predominantly hydrogen)

Helium layer

Carbon core

*The mantle of a **red giant** consists mostly of hydrogen. The next layer is a transitional layer in which hydrogen turns to helium, while further inside the star helium turns to carbon. The carbon inside the core of a red giant reaches temperatures of up to 100 million degrees.*

Red Giants

Red giants represent a particular phase in the development of stars. As a result of its large mass, a star is constantly driven to contract. Initially, however, the radiation energy can withstand the gravitational force. For a long time, these forces remain in a state of equilibrium. However, once the energy supply dwindles, the star is approaching its demise. The inner elements contract. Meanwhile, the outer layers have expanded. They cool off, and the star takes on a reddish appearance. The further development depends on the mass of the dying giant.

Our Sun, once it expands and turns into a red giant, will swallow up the planets Mercury and Venus. At that time, life on Earth, then the planet closest to the Sun, will no longer be possible. Our home planet will no longer have an atmosphere, and all water will have evaporated. However, since another 5 thousand million years will pass before this occurs, it need not concern us immediately. Eventually, our central star will become a white dwarf. In the case of more massive stars, the end is more dramatic. These stars consume

their supply of hydrogen in a few million years. Without this supply of fuel, the star expands and the outer layers cool off. In the interior of the star, pressure forces matter to contract, initiating fusion of helium and carbon. Once this energy is consumed as well, the core consists only of heavy elements. Continued gravitational pressure results in further contraction. This is followed by a collapse in the form of a giant explosion. The only thing that remains is a neutron star or perhaps a black hole.

White Dwarfs

A white dwarf is one possible culmination of the existence of a star. Eventually, this will be the fate of our Sun. First and foremost its size determines the nature of a star's demise.

The so-called critical mass is the equivalent of 1.4 times the mass of the Sun. Stars of this size turn into white dwarfs. Admittedly, there is an exception to this rule. Suns whose mass is considerably less than 10 percent of that of our central star do not have sufficiently hot core temperatures to burn hydrogen. Stars of this type turn into brown dwarfs.

In the case of larger celestial bodies, the stable phase eventually falls apart. The balance of gravitational force and radiation pressure can no longer be maintained. This happens as soon as all available energy is consumed.

Initially, the star expands and sheds its outer layers, sending them whirling out into space. The force of gravity remains victorious, and the remaining core collapses. Despite its large mass, the star shrinks down to the size of a planet.

The remaining matter consists only of an atomic core and electrons. These electrons cannot be compressed. Consequently, any further compression is impossible. In this form, the star can continue to exist for millions of years. It continues to radiate energy, but cannot produce any new energy. In the end, all that remains is a lightless black dwarf.

White dwarf   White dwarf   Planetary nebula

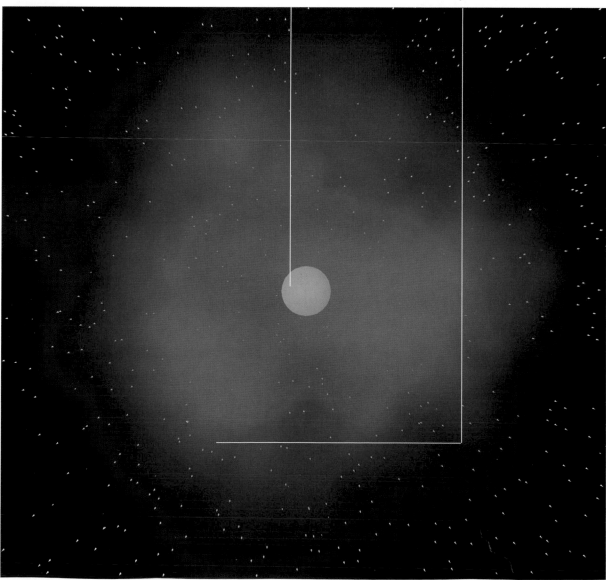

Stars begin their life cycle in the mist. A star that is the same type as our Sun begins to heat up by contracting these nebulae until it finally begins to glow. It remains in this state for approximately 10 thousand million years, until the star expands and turns into a red giant. Later, it shrinks again by shedding its outer layers. These layers produce a planetary mist and expose the core. This celestial object with extremely high density is called a white dwarf. It is not much larger than a planet. Since a white dwarf does not produce any energy, it gradually cools off, eventually turning into a black dwarf.

Binary star "Alpha Centauri"

Neutron Stars

A star whose mass at the end of its life cycle is still greater than 1.4 times that of our Sun turns into a neutron star. Its density becomes so great that electrons and protons fuse to become neutrons. The possibility for the existence of such celestial bodies was predicted on the basis of calculations even before there was any proof of their existence. The density of a neutron star is unimaginable. It is one quadrillion times higher than that of water. No force on Earth could lift up such matter. A pea-sized clump would weigh several million tons.

Standard instruments do not help a great deal when one wants to observe a neutron star. For one, its volume is very limited, and for another, the extreme density delays the diffusion of light. Therefore, astronomers employ actinometry in order to document such celestial bodies. Neutron stars have very high rotational velocities. Depending on their size, they rotate about their axis several times per second. Electrons in the vicinity of a neutron star are hurled out into space at great speeds along the magnetic field lines.

On Earth, this radiation, beams of energy sweeping past the Earth every time a star spins, is registered in the form of short pulses. From this comes the term pulsar. Over time, the rotation velocity decreases and eventually dies down completely.

Binary Stars

Star systems with two or more stars are by no means an exception in the universe. This type of star system occurs in 30 to 50 percent of all cases, depending on which estimate one chooses to go by. Binary stars form a single unit and orbit a common centre of gravity. We are familiar with this phenomenon from Pluto and its moon Charon in our solar system.

However, there also are so-called optical binary stars. For an observer from the Earth, they really look as if they belong together. In actuality, one star is passing the other. Only long-term observation led us to the understanding that these are not actually binary stars that are physically related. This scenario of optical binaries occurs when one of the two celestial bodies travels on a curved path around the other; meanwhile, the actual centre of gravity is between the two or more suns.

Often, binary stars look to us like one individual star. They are so close together that we cannot

Pulsar   Magnetic field lines

Radio wave rays

Binary stars

The term "binary star" refers to two stars of which the physical relation and orbits have been established through long-term observation. They are gravitationally bound and move in an elliptical orbit around the common centre of mass. By contrast, optical binary stars appear to be located next to one another as seen from Earth, but are not physically related.

observe them separately from the Earth.

In many instances, the Hubble Space Telescope has provided a better resolution.

In addition, a measurement of spectral lines can also provide proof. Therefore, astronomers use the term spectroscopic binary stars. It is not necessary for both partners to have the same amount of mass. For instance, it is possible that a main-sequence star forms a unit with a white dwarf.

When the two celestial bodies are near enough to each other, it is possible that the white dwarf takes some matter from its companion. The result would be a nova or, more rarely, a supernova.

Star clusters in a dark nebula

Young blue stars

Star clusters are concentrated collections of stars. We distinguish so-called open clusters, here shown in the dark nebula Barnard 86, and globular clusters with such a density of stars that one can barely distinguish individual stars at their centre.

Star Clusters

Conglomerations of individual stars in various formations are referred to as associations, open clusters, and globular clusters. There are far more individual stars in a globular cluster than in an open cluster.

Associations are essentially open clusters, but with decidedly larger dimensions. The association structure is less clearly defined. However, the number of members is not any higher than in the case of open clusters.

The mean diameter of an open cluster is 4 parsecs. When the diameter exceeds 10 parsecs (sometimes as many as 100 parsecs), astronomers refer to this cluster as an association. These can be observed when they are still relatively young. One can see them only if there are a sufficient number of bright stars. As we know, brighter stars have a shorter life span, since they expend their energy much faster.

While globular clusters are located in the halo of the Milky Way, associations and open clusters remain on the plane of the Milky Way. Together with the spiral arms, they rotate about the common galaxy centre.

Open cluster (Pleiades)

Open clusters are predominantly located along the spiral arms of our Milky Way. Generally, they contain up to 100 stars in a loose formation. A well-known open cluster is called the Pleiades.

The identification I 2 r behind the name of a cluster provides the following information: I = strong concentration, 2 = even distribution of brightness, r = more than 100 stars. Open clusters are located in the main plane of the galaxy. Given that the Milky Way rotates and that the cluster's gravitational forces are not strong enough, open clusters do not become very old. They rip apart and redistribute themselves or turn into moving clusters.

Globular cluster object M 13
(brightest globular cluster in the northern sky)

Open Clusters

As opposed to globular cluster stars, stars in open clusters are very young. Their age is somewhere between a few million and a thousand million years. They are Population 1 stars. In the Milky Way, open clusters occur with much greater frequency than globular clusters. Astronomers estimate that there approximately 10,000; however, by no means all of these can be observed.

The astronomer Robert Trümpler has grouped open clusters on the basis of the following characteristics. These are:

• **Concentration**
• **Brightness**
• **Number of stars**

Concentration: I means strong; IV means weak.

Brightness: 1 means that all stars have the same level of brightness; 3 means that there are many faint stars.

Number of stars: p (poor) means that there are less than 50 stars; r (rich) means that there are more than 100 stars.

**Globular cluster
(mostly old stars)**

Globular clusters contain millions of stars. Generally, density of stars increases towards the centre. The stars inside globular clusters are very old. Presumably, they are as old as the galaxies, in which the globular clusters are located.

Globular Clusters

Globular clusters were formed during the early days of the Milky Way. They are approximately 10 thousand million years old and are located outside the main plane of the galaxy inside its halo. The best known is M 13, located in the constellation Hercules. It is possible to see it with the unaided eye; it looks like a milky spot.

Globular clusters are notable for astoundingly large numbers of stars in relatively small areas. On the average, there are a million stars in a globular cluster with a diameter of 150 light-years. The distance from the Sun is between 2,000 and 300,000 light-years.

Stars in globular clusters are Population 2 stars in accordance with Baade's scheme. These are very old stars. Their age is indicated by the fact that they have no heavy elements. When stars inside globular clusters were formed, shortly after the Big Bang, they could be formed essentially only out the basic elements hydrogen and helium.

Since globular clusters do not contain interstellar matter, the building blocks for stars are missing. No new stars are born inside these clusters. According to estimates, there are about 800 globular clusters in the Milky Way. Of these, we actually know of approximately 150 clusters.

Moving Clusters

Another frequently used term for a moving cluster is "star stream".

Such a cluster is not characterized by a particularly high density of stars, but rather by the fact that its individual members rotate in the same direction and at the same speed.

A familiar example is the Bear Stream. Five of the seven stars that are a part of the Big Dipper are in this stream. The Pleiades and Hyades are other examples of star streams.

Star streams or moving clusters are the after-effects of open clusters. Open clusters do not exist forever. Over time, they lose individual members, so that their density gradually decreases. The remaining stars move towards a common vanishing point or point of convergence.

Moving cluster
(here: the Pleiades, at a distance of approx. 130 parsecs)

Diffuse   Star
nebula masses

Variable Stars

Variable stars are stars with changing degrees of radiation. David Fabrizius was the first to discover such a star 400 years ago. He named it Mira (the Miraculous). It is possible to observe the fluctuations in the degree of brightness in 331-day cycles.

Mira is a pulsating red giant. Its mass is twice that of our Sun; its dimensions range between 200 and 400 times that of the Sun. During the star's expansion phase it not only clearly radiates more energy, it also sheds matter. Such a celestial body cannot sustain itself for a long time in such a state. Astronomers assume that within the next few thousand years Mira will shed its outer layers and eventually turn into a planetary nebula.

Towards the end of a star's life, once all hydrogen in the core has "burned up", the outer layers expand. The star becomes a red giant. The centre contracts and heats up. In the interior, helium turns into carbon in a process of fusion; in the surrounding layer, hydrogen is transformed into helium. Once all helium in the core has been consumed, nuclear fusion occurs in two mantles of the sphere. This is the current state of Mira.

In the case of eruptive variable stars, fluctuations in the degree of brightness occur at irregular intervals. The repetition of a change depends on the strength of the eruption. In the case of regular variable stars, such a repetition is due to the pulsation or differing distribution of brightness on the star's surface. There also are eclipsing variable stars. These, however, are not counted as real variable stars. They are binary stars that cover each other in the course of their rotation. An observer perceives them as a single star with regular pulsation and regular changes in degree of brightness.

Novae

The term "stella nova" comes from Latin and means "new star". Astronomers used to think that a nova was a new star, since sometimes the celestial sphere all of a sudden contained a celestial body that apparently had not existed earlier.

Development of novae

Matter flowing towards the white dwarf   White dwarf   Formation of a thin hot gas disk

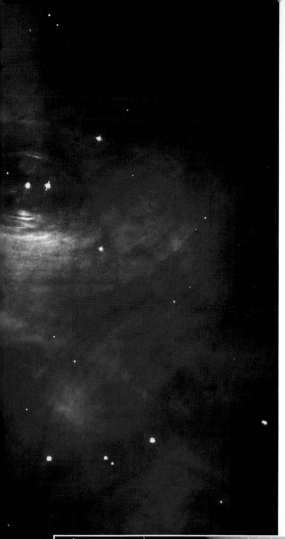

Crab Nebula M1
(Remnants of a supernova from
the year 1054)

In fact, a nova is a star in its final phase. In the course of an immense explosion, a dying sun multiplies its energy radiation.

For instance, in 1572 a nova appeared in the sky. It was so bright that it was visible even during daylight.

How does a nova come about? The basic prerequisite is a binary star system. The two partners in this system must be close together. If one of the two is a white dwarf, it can attract matter from the other star. As a result, helium and hydrogen are deposited on the white dwarf.

As the mass increases, the pressure rises dramatically. The temperature rises to the point where there is a nuclear reaction. During the subsequent explosion, the outer layers are flung out into space. Particles travel at speeds of up 1,000 kilometres per second. However, the destruction does not comprehend the entire binary star system. The amount of material that was burnt off is only a small portion of the total mass. Thus, the system essentially remains in place. This process can repeat itself. For this reason, it has been possible to observe several novae of the same binary star. After the peak of the explosion, which can be reached within a few hours, the brightness gradually decreases again over the following months.

According to various extrapolations, novae appear in the Milky Way approximately three to four dozen times a year.

Supernova

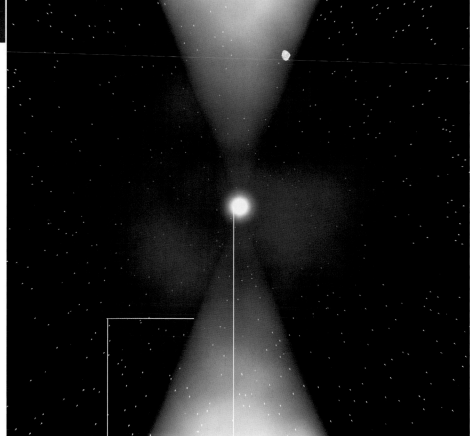

Outer layers flung into space by the explosion

Remaining core after the explosion

Supernovae

The adjective "super" in this context is truly appropriate. The explosion that results in a super nova produces such brightness that it lights up an entire galaxy. The amount of energy released in a few seconds is as much as our Sun will produce over the entire span of its existence as a main-sequence star (10 thousand million years).

According to records kept by Chinese astronomers, they witnessed such a phenomenon in 1054.

Today, astronomers believe that the Cancer Nebula represents the remnants of this supernova.

Supernova is the term used for a star that suddenly erupts into extreme brightness. This occurs at the end of a large-mass star's life. In an enormous explosion, called a supernova, the star's outer layers are flung into space.

There are two types of supernova. Type 1 develops like a nova in a so-called binary star system. A white dwarf receives matter from a neighbouring star. The amount that is passed on is critical. If there is so much matter that the white dwarf can no longer absorb it, it does not fling the outer layers away as in the case of a nova, but rather explodes. Type 2 supernovae most likely were massive stars before the event. When there are no more elements that could produce a nuclear reaction, the existing remnant collapses inside the core. The supernova ex-

plosion occurs within seconds after that collapse. The particles that move away from the centre of the explosion reach speeds of up to 10,000 kilometres per second. Supernovae result in the production of heavy elements. These remain in the expanding cloud produced by the explosion. Eventually, these clouds contribute to the development of new stars. The fact that the subsequent generation is provided with a greater proportion of heavy elements is indicative of the critical role that supernovae play in the development of the universe.

Black Holes

Today, nobody refutes the existence of black holes. While they cannot be seen with optical instruments, their effects are quite evident.

They are a consequence of a supernova explosion. Admittedly, for such a consequence it is necessary that the remaining star remnant still has three times the mass of our Sun. As a result of the force of gravity, this remnant gains in density and turns into a black hole. Ultimately, the gravitational pull is so powerful that nothing can escape, not even light.

If a star comes close to the gravitational field, it is attracted. The transferring particles and gases form a so-called accretion disk around the black hole. This disk rotates at an extremely high speed. The rotation causes heat, which in turn produces energy.

The border of a black hole is called the event horizon. Once matter passes this point, it disappears completely and irretrievably. The greater the mass, the more powerful will be the gravitational pull; in other words, the more food is offered to the insatiable monster, the more ravenous it becomes. It is not possible to offer precise physical figures regarding the density of black holes. Essentially, it is immensely high, just like the pressure and the temperature.

Black hole

I. Particle-antiparticle pair

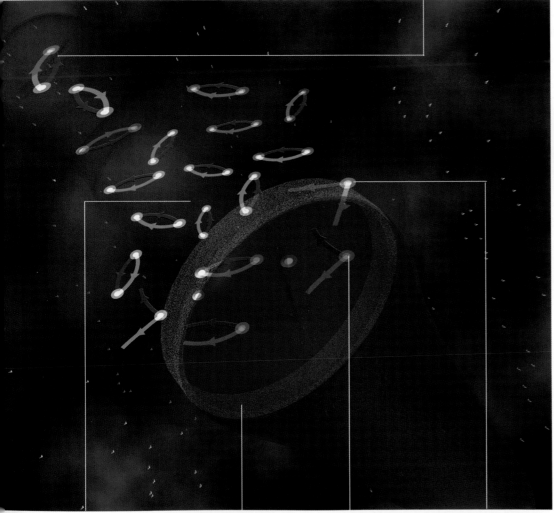

II. Particle pairs are sucked in by gravity.

Glowing ring consisting of escaping particles and antiparticles

III. Particle pair split up by extremely curved space

IV. Antiparticles can escape

Black holes have enormous gravitational force. Their matter is so dense that not even light can escape. For instance, when nuclear particles such as electrons, together with their antiparticles, are sucked into the gravitational pull of a black hole, a particle will fall into the hole. Its partner escapes and forms a glowing ring around the black hole. Black holes shrink when particles escape from it without having shed their energy. They begin to dissipate until they finally self-destruct in an enormous explosion.

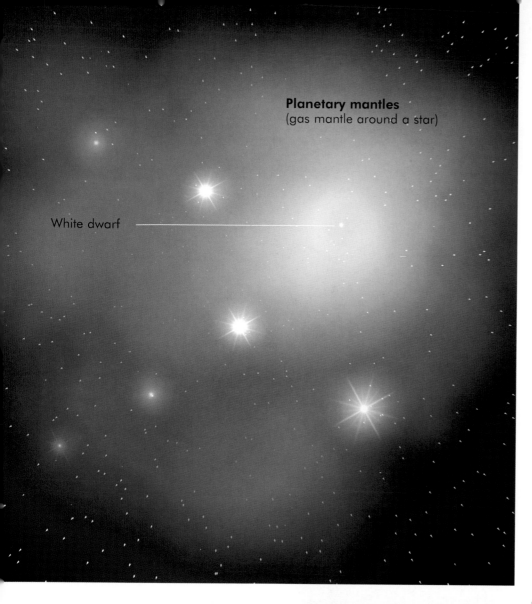

Planetary mantles
(gas mantle around a star)

White dwarf

The term planetary nebula refers to a gas cloud that has an aging star without its outer mantle at its centre. Generally, such a star is so faint that it often can barely be seen. The energy radiation of the star remnant illuminates the gas, and this remains visible over several tens of thousands of years.

power of the dying sun wanes, and the nebula becomes fainter and fainter.

After several tens of thousands of years, it is an almost imperceptible gas mantle. The star itself turns into a white dwarf. The mantle has once again turned into interstellar matter, from which new stars could develop, provided there is a sufficient amount of matter available.

Planetary Nebula

The term "planetary nebula" is misleading. The poor visibility calls to mind the appearance of planets. In fact, however, this is a mantle surrounding an aging star.

To date, approximately 1,000 of these planetary nebulae have been discovered in our Milky Way. Their life span is at most 50,000 years. When a star approaches its end, it often turns into a red giant. A strong stellar wind carries the outer layers away.

The star compresses and the resulting heat radiates so strongly that the rejected layers are illuminated. The planetary mist expands and reaches a diameter of up to several light-years. Over time, the

Planetary nebula M 2–9

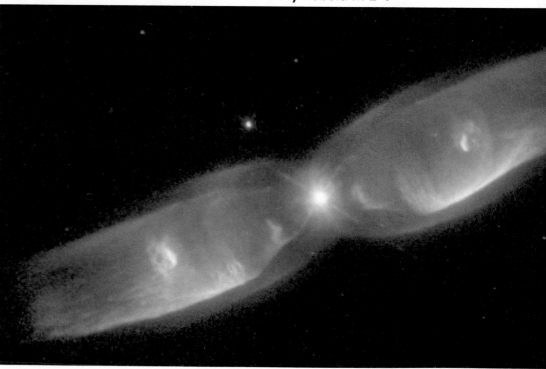

Images of the Zodiac

Due to the enormous distances involved, observers on Earth gain the impression that all stars in the sky are at the same distance from the Earth. Already during the age of antiquity, human beings described groupings of stars that they could observe with the unaided eye as constellations. They assigned these groups of stars the names of heroes, gods and animals, as well as items from daily life.

During the lifetime of Claudius Ptolemy (110–178 AD), 48 constellations were known. In the 17th century, another 12 in the northern hemisphere and approximately 50 in the southern hemisphere were added. Today, we know of 88 constellations in the celestial sphere. Twelve of these are the images of the zodiac. Another 27 constellations are located north of the zodiac, and 49 south of the zodiac.

The zodiac is the area, approximately 20 degrees wide, that spans the celestial sphere and provides the background for the ecliptic. From the vantage point of the Earth, the ecliptic is the "street" along which the Sun appears to be travelling along the celestial sphere in the course of one year.

Inside the zodiac, one can find the following images: Ram (Aries), Bull (Taurus), Twins (Gemini), Crab (Cancer), Lion (Leo), Virgin (Virgo), Scales (Libra), Scorpion (Scorpio), Archer (Sagittarius), Goat (Capricorn), Water Bearer (Aquarius), and Fishes (Pisces).

Orientation

The four main points of the compass – north, south, east and west – are of great help in orienting oneself in the sky. The borderline between the celestial sphere and the surface of our planet is called the horizon. The point of the celestial sphere located directly above us is called the zenith.

In order to locate a particular star, it is easiest to begin with the northerly direction. There is a star near the northern celestial pole that can be observed easily with the unaided eye: Polaris, also known as the Polar Star.

It is the main star in the constellation of the Little Dipper/Little Bear (Ursa Minor) and only about one and a half Moon widths from the exact North Pole. In order to find it, one first would look for that constellation that is the most memorable, that is the Big Dipper. It is visible throughout the year; therefore, it is described as a circumpolar star.

Once one has located the Big Dipper, one can draw a line connecting the two stars forming the back of the Dipper. By extending this line five times, one comes to Polaris. This is true throughout all the seasons, regardless of the position of the Big Dipper. If one draws a vertical line towards the horizon, one has located the northerly direction. Starting at this point, west is 90 degrees towards

Mirror telescope

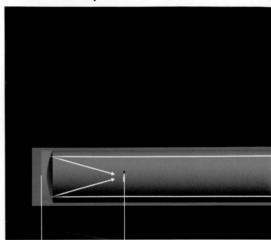

Mirror   Primary focal point

Since the days of Galileo, telescopes and other optical instruments have been used for observation of the sky. The most frequently used instruments are so-called mirror telescopes, today available in a variety of designs.

the left, east is 90 degrees towards the right, and south is 180 degrees ahead.

In addition to the main points of the compass, there are numerous transitional directions, beginning with north and including north-north-east, north-east, east-north-east, east, and continuing in this vein for all the main directions.

Polaris

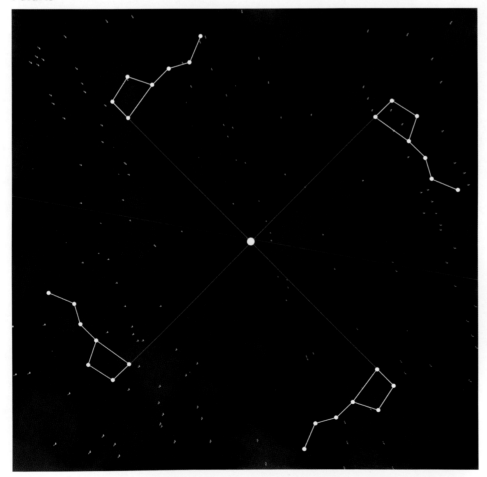

Astronomical Instruments

Many astronomical observations can be undertaken with the un-aided eye. For instance, one could begin by locating, grouping, and coordinating individual stars and constellations. However, if one wanted to undertake more precise observations, optical devices would become indispensable.

The first optical telescope was designed in 1608 by a Dutch optician called Hans Lipperhey. Galileo Galilei heard about this invention and built his own telescope in the following year, using it for his astronomical studies. At that time, he already discovered the four moons of Jupiter. He was now able to recognize sunspots as well as mountains on the lunar surface.

The often used refractor essentially consists of a "tubus" – the tube-shaped body of the telescope. A mirror or several lenses at the end of this telescope body reflect the image of the observed object. At a certain distance (focal length) behind the lens, a reversed image appears. Using an ocular, the image can be enlarged for closer examination. Depending on focal points and lens diameters, there are different degrees of enlargement and focus available.

Newton reflector

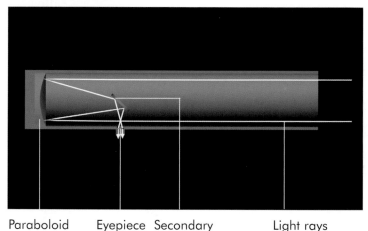

Paraboloid concave mirror   Eyepiece   Secondary mirror   Light rays

The Newton reflector is a mirror telescope with a secondary mirror in front of the primary focal point. Just before the unification of the rays reflected by a paraboloid primary mirror, these rays are deflected by a flat mirror, inclined at a 45-degree angle toward the optical axis and projected out of the side of the telescope body.

Lens telescope

yepiece

cal point   Convex lens   Objective

Lens telescopes, also called refractors, are telescopes where the lens is convex. At a certain distance, referred to as the focal point, a reversed image is produced, which can be enlarged and observed through the eyepiece.

In addition to refractors, there are mirror telescopes in various designs. The Newton mirror is used frequently. A paraboloid concave mirror reflects the light of an object. A reversed image is produced at the focal point.

In order to be able to study this image, a secondary flat mirror is installed just in front of the primary mirror at a 45-degree angle towards the optical axis of the telescope. This deflects the light out of the telescope sideways; in other words, the image plane is positioned sideways, and the object can be studied through an eyepiece attached on the side.

Other mirror telescopes include the Cassegrain telescope and telescopes that use the catadioptric system. Over the past few years, these have become increasingly popular among amateur astronomers because they are compact and hence easily transportable, and furthermore produce good results.

Binoculars are also suitable for astronomical observations. They even have advantages, given the wide visual field they provide. They are especially well-suited for the observation of larger objects, such as comets with their tails or larger clusters such as the Pleiades. They can even be used to make out details on the lunar surface. Binoculars are constructed on the basis of the same principle as optical telescopes.

Radio telescopes record radio waves emitted by celestial bodies. As early as 1931, a physicist by the name of Karl Guthe Janky, while investigating disruptions of radio signals, discovered that this had to be caused by radio waves from outer space.

Catadioptric system

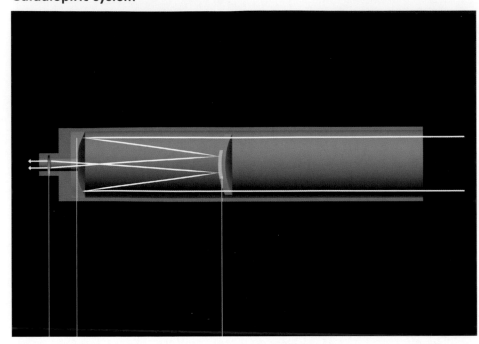

Eyepiece   Mirror   Lens with reflective coating
                          or convex mirror

In the catadioptric system, the main mirror is generally polished to a spherical shape. The light passes through a thick meniscus lens with reflective coating in place of the secondary mirror.

for Radio Astronomy. The diameter of its paraboloid antenna is 100 metres.

Another variant of a radio telescope is an enormous construction in a hollow in the northwestern mountains of Puerto Rico. The Arecibo Ionospheric Observatory is shaped like a plate with a diameter of 305 metres. A huge antenna above the plate is kept in position by towers on the outside.

Soon scientists discovered that these came from a specific area of the Milky Way. Meanwhile, significant progress in radio astronomy occurred only after World War II.

Today, a radio telescope essentially consists of an antenna system, an amplifier and an integrator with a registration device. The antenna, which can be relatively large, captures electromagnetic rays from the universe.

A small antenna, mounted inside the focal point, collects the rays, amplifies them, and transforms them, so that finally they can be transmitted as signals to the registration device, where their strength is recorded.

The largest radio telescope of this type in Germany is in Eiffelberg; it is part of the Max-Planck Institute

Cassegrain telescope

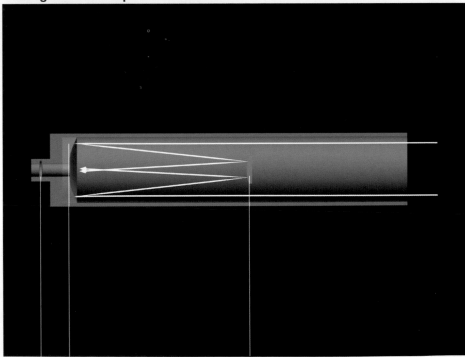

Eyepiece   Paraboloid mirror   Secondary
            (pierced)   mirror

In a Cassegrain telescope, a convex hyperboloid mirror is attached in front of the primary focal point. Light from the primary mirror is reflected by a secondary mirror through a hole pierced into the primary mirror, thus reaching the eyepiece at the tail end of the telescope.

Seasons

The time measure "year" applies to the time it takes for our planet to orbit once around the Sun. This orbit can be perceived indirectly by observing the apparent movement of the Sun along the celestial sphere. The year has different lengths, depending on the respective point of reference one uses to observe the Earth's orbit and the assumed movement of the Sun.

The tropical year refers to the interval between two passages of the Sun through the vernal equinox. The length of this year is 365.242199 Ephemeridae days (an established unit of time).

The sidereal year refers to the interval between two passages of the Sun past one and the same fixed star and is about as long as the tropical year, that is, 365.256366 days.

Other definitions of a year's length are the anomalistic year (365.259626 days) and the eclipse year (346.620032 days).

Our seasons are the result of the breakdown of the tropical year into four time spans that are dependent on the apparent path of the Sun across the celestial sphere.

However, they are actually determined by those points in time when the Sun, travelling on its apparent path, crosses the celestial equator from south to north (approximately 21 March) and from north to south (approximately 23 September). These two points in time are called equinoxes.

The other two points in time, the so-called solstices, refer to that moment when the Sun, travelling on its apparent path, arrives at the points of its greatest northern and southern deviation respectively from the celestial equator. The different lengths of the individual seasons are caused by differences

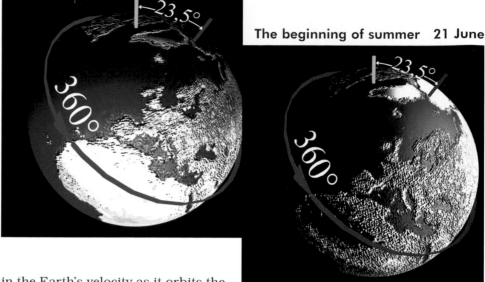

The beginning of spring   21 March

The beginning of summer   21 June

in the Earth's velocity as it orbits the Sun. The impact of spring, summer and fall is noticeable especially in the temperate zones of our planet. At the North and South Poles, there are only two seasons – polar day and polar night.

The Earth's axis of rotation is not vertical towards its orbital plane, but rather inclined at a 23.5-degree angle. As the Earth orbits the Sun, the solar altitude changes. This term refers to the changing angle at which the Sun's rays hit the Earth. In the winter, the Sun's rays hit the Earth at a flat angle. Warmth is spread out across a wider area; therefore, it is colder than in the summer.

- Spring from 21 March to 20 June
- Summer from 21 June to 22 September

- Fall from 23 September to 20 December
- Winter from 21 December to 20 March

On 21 March and 23 September, day and night are equal in length (equinoxes). 21 June is the longest day and the shortest night of the year (summer solstice). While it is spring in the northern hemisphere, it is fall in the southern hemisphere; when we have summer, it is winter there.

Seasons do not change abruptly on the respective astronomically determined dates. Changes in the length of sunlight and solar altitude, combined with other factors affecting weather conditions, such as particular mountain formations or ocean currents, produce gradual seasonal shifts.

The beginning of fall 23 September

The beginning of winter 21 December

Solar Orbit

The Earth orbits the Sun over the course of one year. If it were possible to see the stars during daylight, one could follow the Sun's apparent path across the sky.

It is possible, however, to follow the Sun's path directly by watching the stars in the western sky at nightfall over the course of an entire year. For instance, if one were to begin with such a course of observation in April, the constellations Orion, Big Dog (Canis Major), Little Dog (Canis Minor), Charioteer (Auriga), and Bull (Taurus) would be prominent. Gradually, these images would sink lower until they finally disappear altogether.

Sun's path

Over the course of a year, the Sun travels past the various constellations in the sky. These can be divided roughly into winter, summer, fall, and spring constellations.

Day and night hours

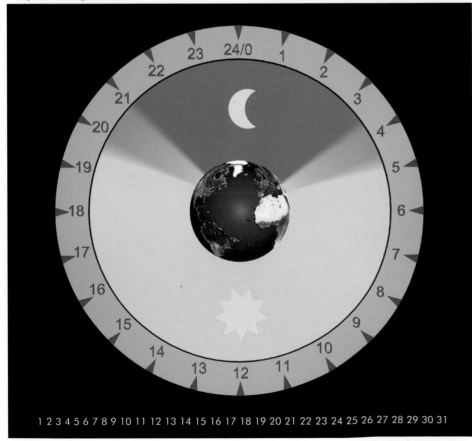

May

They would reappear gradually in late summer. In the meantime, the spring, summer and fall constellations would be visible. In an approximate fashion, human beings have assigned the various constellations to the respective seasons.

The background for the Sun's apparent path across the celestial hemisphere is referred to as the zodiac. The Sun's apparent path is called the ecliptic.

Day and night are the result of the Earth's rotation about its axis. The length of a day, in other words, the time span between sunrise and sunset, changes over the course of a year. Day and night times vary in length depending on the angle of the Sun's rays as it travels on its apparent path.

Lunar Orbit

The Moon rotates in an east-west direction around the Earth. The Earth has the same rotational direction and the same direction in its orbit of the Sun. One lunar orbit takes 27.8 days. It takes the Moon exactly the same amount of time to rotate once about its axis.

For this reason, we always see the same side of the Moon. The proper term for this is "bound rotation". We are familiar with this phenomenon in connection with the double planet Pluto/Charon. The Earth and the Moon, just like the outermost planet in our solar system and its moon, orbit around the same centre of gravity. Since the Earth's mass is so much greater than that of the Moon, this centre of gravity is not between the two celestial bodies but rather inside the Earth itself.

The lunar orbit is not circular but elliptical. The difference between the point of shortest distance and greatest distance is approximately 12 percent. The lunar axis is tilted slightly towards the vertical of the orbital plane. The Moon's revolutionary velocity is also subject to certain fluctuations. Closer towards the Earth, the Moon travels more rapidly than when it is farther away. As a result of these librations (oscillating lunar movements), portions of the side of the Moon facing away from the Earth are sometimes visible.

It is possible to see almost 60 percent of the entire lunar surface; however, never more than 50 percent at the same time. During its orbit, our satellite passes through phases from New Moon to Full Moon. These phases are caused by the changing angle of the sunlight.

At New Moon, our satellite is in conjunction with the Sun. At night, the side of the Moon not lit up by the Sun is turned towards the Earth; therefore, we cannot see it. During

Phases of the Moon

The Moon, which reflects the sunlight, appears to the Earth-bound observer in different phases, from a crescent moon to a full moon.

Moon   Moon   Earth   Sun

the first quarter (waxing Moon), half of the side facing the Earth is lit up. We can see the Moon during the first hours of the night.

During Full Moon, we can see the Moon in its entirety throughout the night. It is in opposition to the Sun, and the hemisphere facing us is completely illuminated.

During the last quarter (waning Moon), we can see only half of the planet during the second half of the night.

The transition between the illuminated and the dark side of the Moon is called "terminator". This term comes from Latin and means "border" or "bordering".

Solar and Lunar Eclipses

The complete obliteration of a celestial body by another is called an eclipse. The small Moon can cover the large Sun, because the apparent sizes are practically identical. The closeness to the Sun compensates for the difference in size. When the Moon is in conjunction, in other words between the Earth and the Sun, a solar eclipse can occur. However, given the orbital tilt of the Moon, an eclipse does not occur at every New Moon. This phenomenon occurs only when the lunar orbital plane and the ecliptic plane cross each other.

Solar eclipses can be observed only in a limited area, and they last at most seven minutes and 40 seconds. When the Moon is in opposition to the Sun, a lunar eclipse can occur. This phenomenon can be observed, because the Moon does not disappear altogether.

The light is practically diverted by Earth's atmosphere. When our satellite travels through the partial shadow of the Earth, the result is a partial eclipse. The visibility of a total lunar eclipse is not limited spatially. Wherever a Full Moon would be visible, one would also be able to observe a lunar eclipse.

The space of time during which one can observe a lunar eclipse is several hours, significantly longer than the time during which one might be able to observe a solar eclipse.

Solar eclipse   Moon in front of the Sun

Sun

Moon

Earth

A solar eclipse occurs when the Moon is between the Sun and the Earth. Its shadow hits the Earth's surface. For the observer on Earth, the Sun appears to be covered by the Moon. We distinguish between total, partial, and ring-shaped solar eclipses. This depends on the observer's location as well as on the relative positioning of the Earth, Sun and Moon.

Lunar eclipse

Moon behind the Earth

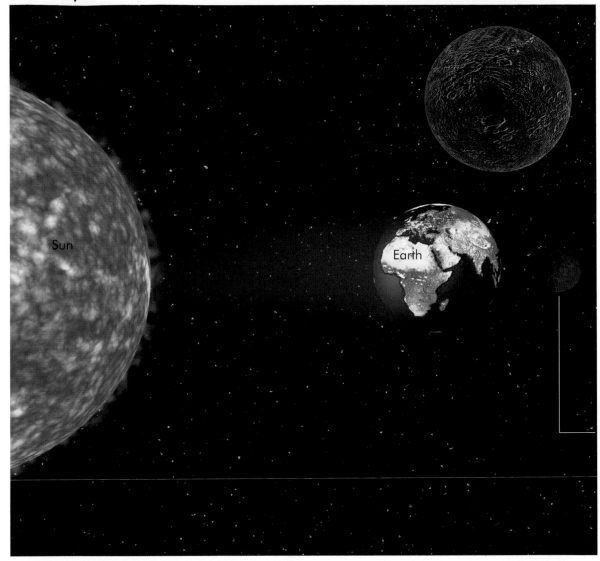

Sun

Earth

Moon

A lunar eclipse can occur only when the full moon crosses the Earth's orbit. At that point, the Moon enters into the Earth's shadow cone. The Moon does not become completely invisible, but is instead bathed in a reddish brown light. This is due to the fact that a portion of the sunlight at the edge of the Earth is diverted by the atmosphere into Earth's shadow.

Degrees of Brightness

Stars have always been assigned different classes of magnitude. For instance, Polaris is a category 2 star. This is not a reference to its diameter, nor is it a classification of its real luminosity. Instead, the decisive factor in this classification of magnitude is its apparent brightness in the sky.

In the age of antiquity, the stars in the universe were assigned to six different classes of magnitude according to their respective degrees of brightness. The brightest stars were category 1 stars. Those stars that one could just barely see with the unaided eye under the most advantageous circumstances were classified as category 6 stars.

According to this classification scheme, a category 1 star was 100 times brighter than a category 6 star. Hence, a category 2 star is about 2.5 times fainter than a category 1 star. Once these categories had been determined, it became necessary to expand the classification scheme to include especially bright stars in minus categories. Thus, the brightest star in the sky, Vega in the constellation Lyra, is a category 0 star, while the Sun is even further down in the minus classification.

Estimating degrees of brightness of stars is a matter of practice. This should not be confused with the absolute brightness of stars, which represents real luminosity. That can be calculated on the basis of the apparent brightness a celestial body would have at a particular distance. For stars, this unit of distance was set at 10 parsecs.

GLOSSARY

Accretion disk
A disk consisting of extremely heated gas masses. Taking on a spiral shape, these gas masses are sucked into a black hole.

Active galaxy
A galaxy with strong eruptions in the centre.

Anomalistic year
365.25962 days. The time span between two passages of Earth through its perihelion.

Aphelion
The farthest point from the Sun on the orbit of a planet.

Apogee
The point farthest away from Earth on the elliptical orbit of the Moon.

Asteroid
Small planet, planetoid.

Astronomical unit, AU
The mean distance of Earth from the Sun. 1 AU = 149,565,800 kilometres.

Atmosphere
The gas layer surrounding a celestial body.

Atom
The smallest particle of an element that can be involved in a chemical reaction. The main portion of the atomic mass is concentrated in its nucleus, which has a radius of a millionth of a millionth centimetre.

Axial tilt
The angle that a planet's rotation axis makes with the line perpendicular to the plane of its orbit.

Big Bang
The explosion of the universe, beginning at a state of unimaginable density. It is assumed that this occurred 10 to 15 thousand million years ago.

Black hole
Remains of a star in which matter collapses to such an extent and with such intense gravity that even light cannot escape.

Black mini-hole
A very small black hole with the mass of a mountain but the size of an atom. It is assumed that such black mini-holes were formed during the Big Bang.

Catadioptric
Telescope with a corrective lens in front of a mirror (e.g. Schmidt-Cassegrain Telescope and Maksutow Telescope).

Comets
Comets are sometimes called dirty snowballs or "icy mudballs". They are a mixture of ices (both water and frozen gases) and dust that for some reason was not incorporated into planets when the solar system was formed. Active comets are notable for their distinctive dust tails, the most prominent part of a comet to the unaided eye, up to 10 million km long and composed of smoke-sized dust particles driven off the nucleus by escaping gases.

Conjunction
The point where a planetary orbit or the lunar orbit crosses the ecliptic (the plane of Earth's orbit).

Constellation
A group of stars that forms a recognizable pattern.

Convection
Turbulent convection involves a transfer of heat and energy in stars, disrupting the thermodynamic balance in certain layers; hotter matter rises, while cooler matter sinks down.

Cosmic microwave background radiation
Homogeneous and isotropic microwave radiation surrounding us. It is assumed that this is a remnant of the fireball phase of the Big Bang.

Cosmology
Science that takes the universe as a whole as its object of inquiry.

Declination
The arc of measurement in degrees north or south of the celestial equator, i.e. the celestial equivalent of latitude. The celestial equator is zero degrees, while the celestial north and south poles are 90 and –90 degrees, respectively.

Doppler effect
The shift of an object's spectrum because it moves toward or away from Earth.

Dust
Microscopically small grains of dust in space that absorb starlight. This dust is the soot left over from dying stars. Grains of dust can conglomerate into huge dark clouds.

Dwarf star
A star with a smaller diameter than the Sun.

Earth's shadow
Earth projects a shadow into space. During a lunar eclipse, this shadow becomes visible on the passing moon for a brief period of time.

Eccentricity, orbital
Astronomers use the concept of orbital eccentricity to express how round or elliptical a planet's orbit is.

Eclipse year
The time period between two passages of the Sun through a certain conjunction of the Moon.

Ecliptic
The orbit along the celestial sphere on which the Sun appears to be moving over the course of one year, while the Earth is orbiting the Sun.

Electromagnetic waves
Radiation consisting of electrical and magnetic fields and moving with the speed of light.

Electron
Lightweight subatomic particle with a negative charge that revolves around the nucleus of an atom.

Ephemeridae
The coordinates of a star at a particular point in time.

Ergosphere
Turbulent area around a black hole between the static border and the outer event horizon, in which everything is captured; no particles can remain at rest within this stationary limit.

Erosion
Destruction of the surface of a planet by water, wind, temperature and other natural occurrences.

Evening star
The bright planet Venus during its greatest eastern elongation.

Event horizon
An imaginary surface forming the edge of a black hole, inside of which the recession velocity reaches the speed of light.

Expansion of the universe
The greater the distance of a galaxy from us, the faster it is moving further away.

Fixed star
A term coming from the Latin stella fixa (fixed star), used to refer to a star apparently fixed in the celestial sphere from the observer's point of view.

Flare
The eruption of magnetic radiation on the surface of a star or the Sun.

Galaxies
Star systems that consist of a conglomeration of hundreds of millions of stars; comparable to our Milky Way.

Geocentric
A worldview with the Earth at the centre of the universe.

Giant star
A star with a much larger diameter than the Sun.

Gravitation
A term used in physics to describe the force with which masses attract each other, also referred to as gravity. The Earth and the Moon are subject to mutual gravitational forces.

Heliocentric
A worldview that places the Sun at the centre of the universe.

Hertzsprung-Russel-Diagram
This diagram is used for registering the absolute brightness of stars in reference to their spectral types.

Horizon system
The primary circle of the horizon together with the two poles, zenith and nadir above and below the horizon, form this astronomical system of coordinates.

Hubble's Law
The ratio between galaxies' recession velocity and their distance. This law is based on the expansion of the universe.

Hydrogen combustion
In hydrogen combustion, hydrogen turns into helium; this process is the energy source of many stars and the Sun.

Inner planets
The planets inside Earth's orbit: Mercury and Venus.

Last stable orbit
The orbit closest to a black hole along which something can move without falling into the black hole.

Light-year
A light-year is the distance covered by light, travelling at 300,000 kilometres per second, in one year.

Local Group
A group of approximately 20 galaxies, dominated by our Milky Way.

Luminosity
The energy radiated by the entire surface of a star in a given time unit.

Magma
Hot glowing lava below the surface of planets. It is called lava when it reaches the surface as a result of volcanic eruptions.

Main-sequence star
In the Hertzsprung-Russel Diagram, this is a star inside the main sequence. Most stars in our Milky Way are main-sequence stars.

Mass
The amount of matter in a body. On Earth, the mass of a body corresponds to its weight.

Meteor
Popularly called a "shooting star" or a "falling star", a meteor is actually an object usually ranging from the size of a dust particle to a rock that enters Earth's atmosphere and is heated by the friction of air resistance. Most meteors originate from comets.

Meteorite
A meteor that is large enough to survive its passage through the atmosphere and hit the ground.

Milky Way
Our galaxy. A giant galaxy with hundreds of thousand millions of stars.

Minor planet
Small planet, planetoid.

Morning star
The bright planet Venus during its greatest western elongation.

Nadir
The lowest point of the celestial sphere.

Neutrino
A subatomic particle without electrical charge and without mass, formed in central regions of stars and in nuclear reactions during supernova explosions. Documented in the case of the Sun and the supernova 1987A.

Neutron
An uncharged subatomic particle in the atomic nucleus.

Neutron stars
Collapsed stars with a diameter of 5 to 10 kilometres.

Nova
A star that suddenly and explosively increases its luminosity a million times. This process is initiated by matter that falls from a satellite star onto a white dwarf.

Nuclear Fusion
A nuclear reaction, the released energy of which makes stars glow. In this process, which involves tremendous heat and pressure, hydrogen atoms, for instance, are fused and transformed into helium.

Open cluster
These clusters are located on the disks of spiral galaxies and consist of loose clusters of young large-mass stars.

Paraboloid mirror
A reflecting mirror in the form of a rotation paraboloid.

Parallax
The apparent shift of a nearby star, due to a change in the observer's position, i.e., the yearly orbit of Earth around the Sun, causing a perspective change.

Parsec
Abbreviation for parallax and second; the distance from the Sun at which an astronomical unit becomes visible at 1 arcsecond as seen from the Earth. 1 pc = 206,265 AU.

Perigee
Closest point of the Moon to the Earth.

Perihelion
The point closest to the Sun on the elliptical orbit of a planet.

Photon
A term from quantum theory for subatomic particles emitting electromagnetic radiation. Photons form their own family of subatomic particles.

Planet
A celestial body that does not radiate its own light, but rather only reflects the light of a central star that it orbits.

Planetary nebula
A layer of gas that is set aglow by a hot massive central star. This layer is produced when a star sheds its outer layers during its red giant phase.

Polaris
Also known as the North Star, Polar Star, or Pole Star, it is the main star in the constellation of the Little Bear/Little Dipper (Ursa Minor).

Positron
Positrons are positively charged anti-particles of the electron. When annihilating with electrons, their mass is converted into gamma ray photons.

Proper motion
The relative movement of stars in the sky, due to their orbiting within the Milky Way.

Proton
Positively charged subatomic particles. Together with neutrons, they form the atomic nucleus.

Pulsar
Pulsars are neutron stars. Radiation beams are sent by radio sources at regular intervals.

Quasar (quasi-stellar radio source)
The extremely bright core of an active young distant galaxy. The outer areas are often too weak to be visible.

Radiation
A form of energy diffusion consisting of waves or particles.

Radio astronomy
An area of astronomy that focuses on the study of the radio waves emitted by cosmic bodies and cosmic space (background radiation).

Radio telescope
Receiving device used to capture radio waves sent by objects in space.

Recession velocity
The speed with which a body travels in order to escape the gravitational pull on the surface of a star or a planet (hence also referred to as escape velocity).

Red Giant
An aging star, the outer layers of which have expanded and cooled off.

Redshift
When a star moves away, the spectral lines shift toward red. This is understood as part of the process of the recession of galaxies and the expansion of the universe.

Reflector
A telescope with a mirror lens.

Refractor
A telescope with a convex lens.

Regolith
An unstable surface layer that is the product of a mixture of rocks, dust, and fragments caused by the impact of meteorites. On the Moon, the regolith layer is 15 centimetres thick. Other celestial bodies (those without atmosphere) also have a regolith layer.

Sheepdog moons
A term used for moons or satellites that apparently – such as in the case of Saturn's F-ring – "guard" and keep the ring parts together just like a dog herding sheep.

Sidereal year
The time period between two passages of the Sun past a certain fixed star. This year has 365.25636 days.

Spaghettification
When a body falls into a black hole, gravity stretches it.

Star cluster
A system of stars that have a common origin and are linked by their gravitational pull.

Static border
A border near a black hole; once inside that border nothing can escape.

Stellar black hole
A black hole that was formed by a supernova, the explosion of a large-mass star.

Super cluster
A very large cluster of galaxies or a group of galaxy clusters.

Supergiant
A very bright large star.

Superheavy black hole
A black hole found at the centre of a galaxy. Such holes are formed by material that falls into the core of the galaxy.

Supernova
The sudden explosion of a large-mass star.

Terminator
The borderline between light and shadow and day and night on a celestial body that does not produce light of its own (planet, moon).

Triple system
A multiple system consisting of three stars. Roughly 80 percent of all stars are in binary or multiple star systems.

Trojans
Planetoids on the orbit of Jupiter.

Tropical year
The time period between two passages of the Sun through the vernal equinox. This year is 365.24219 days.

Variable stars
A star with variable radiation.

White hole
An object that ejects matter and energy, in other words, the exact opposite of a black hole.

White dwarf
A small dying star that continues to cool off until it has reached the final phase.

Wormhole
An object with two exits, each leading to a different area of the universe and connected by a tunnel, inside of which motion in both directions can be assumed.

Zenith
Crown of the celestial sphere.

Zodiac
The twelve constellations in the sky along the ecliptic within which the Sun and the planets move.

Zodiacal light
A light cone created by the dispersion of light off small dust grains spread out in the solar system, which can be observed directly before sunrise and directly after sunset.

INDEX